ENERGY:
FROM SURPLUS TO SCARCITY?

The Proceedings of the Institute of Petroleum Summer Meeting, 'Energy: From Surplus to Scarcity?' held at Harrogate, 5–8 June 1973

ENERGY: FROM SURPLUS TO SCARCITY?

Edited by

K. A. D. INGLIS

Economic Adviser, Public Affairs,
British Petroleum Co. Ltd, London, UK

A HALSTED PRESS BOOK

JOHN WILEY & SONS
New York – Toronto

PUBLISHED IN THE U.S.A. AND CANADA BY
HALSTED PRESS
A DIVISION OF JOHN WILEY & SONS INC., NEW YORK

> The symbol I.P. on this book means that the
> text has been officially accepted as authoritative
> by the Institute of Petroleum, Great Britain

Library of Congress Cataloging in Publication Data
Main entry under title:

Energy: from surplus to scarcity?

"A Halsted Press book."
"The proceedings of the Institute of Petroleum
summer meeting."
   1. Power resources—Congresses. I. Inglis,
K. A. D., ed. II. Institute of Petroleum, London.
III. Title.
HD9540.1.E45   333.7   73-22112
ISBN 0-470-42731-0

WITH 50 ILLUSTRATIONS AND 30 TABLES

© APPLIED SCIENCE PUBLISHERS LTD 1974

Printed in Great Britain by Galliard (Printers) Ltd Great Yarmouth

Contents

List of Contributors

H. J. ALKEMA
*Head, Technological Forecasting, Shell International Petroleum Co. Ltd,
Shell Centre, London, UK*

D. H. BROADBENT
Director of Special Projects, National Coal Board, London, UK

L. G. BROOKES
*Economics and Planning Branch, United Kingdom Atomic Energy Authority,
London, UK*

G. CHANDLER
President, The Institute of Petroleum, London, UK

M. W. CLEGG
*Divisional Manager, Planning Systems, Central Developmental Planning
Department, British Petroleum Co. Ltd, London, UK*

P. F. CORBETT
*Marketing Services Manager, Gas Division, International Sales Department,
British Petroleum Co. Ltd, London, UK*

T. F. GASKELL
Scientific Adviser, Public Affairs, British Petroleum Co. Ltd, London, UK

ADRIAN HAMILTON
Energy Editor, The Financial Times

K. A. D. INGLIS
Economic Adviser, Public Affairs, British Petroleum Co. Ltd, London, UK

D. C. ION
Formerly British Petroleum Co. Ltd, London, UK

D. C. LESLIE
*Professor of Nuclear Engineering, Queen Mary College, University of
London, UK*

JOHN H. LICHTBLAU
*Executive Director, Petroleum Industry Research Foundation, Inc., New
York, USA*

E. V. NEWLAND
Long Range Corporate Planning, Shell International Petroleum Co. Ltd, Shell Centre, London, UK

EDITH PENROSE
Professor of Economics, School of Oriental and African Studies, University of London, UK

M. H. ROTHKOPF
Formerly Shell International Petroleum Co. Ltd

A. R. UBBELOHDE, C.B.E., F.R.S.
Professor of Thermodynamics, Imperial College of Science and Technology, University of London, UK

H. DE VRIES
Economic Researcher, Koninklijke/Shell-Laboratorium, Amsterdam, The Netherlands

Abbreviations

aai	Average annual increment
bd	Barrels per day
cfd	Cubic feet per day
mbd	Million barrels per day
mbdoe	Million barrels per day oil equivalent
mcfd	Million cubic feet per day
mtce	Million tons coal equivalent
mtfoe	Million tons fuel oil equivalent
uso	Unit sent out from station

Opening Address

K. A. D. INGLIS

Chairman of Organising Committee

Ladies and Gentlemen, may I welcome you to the 1973 Institute of Petroleum Summer Meeting. The nature of this meeting has over the years changed considerably. At one time it was regarded basically as a social gathering with a serious excuse provided for the social encounter that this led to. Now I think the emphasis is more strongly upon the content of our discussions. When the Institute first considered an appropriate subject to be discussed at this meeting—that was a matter of about eight months ago—there were considerable doubts as to whether the topic we are going to discuss over the next three days would be relevant, appropriate or capable of being discussed openly and freely. I think from the evidence that we have from the last few days, and indeed from the last few months, that our views on the choice of this topic—Energy, from Surplus to Scarcity?—were correct, and may I apologise for the printing error on the folder within which your papers are contained—the question mark has been dropped; this was not a change in attitude of the part of the Institute, but purely a printer's error.

The question mark is being raised in virtually every part of the world at the moment. I do not think we could have done better than hold this meeting within a matter of weeks of President Nixon's energy message. I think our foresight is rewarded by the fact that this is to my knowledge the first open meeting, first open conference of this sort held in the United Kingdom on what in the eyes of the public, in the eyes of the media, has become a question of absolutely critical importance. We intentionally did not entitle this meeting 'Energy Crisis?' but whether we believe that we are in a situation of energy crisis or not, to my mind does not matter, because there is a widespread belief in many important centres that we are confronting both in the short and medium term, and in the long term, something which can be categorised as a crisis. I think part of our purpose in the next three days is to see whether this is justified or not, and I am quite certain that many of us believe it is not justified. But in the face of an attitude that is spreading world-wide on the part of the public, those of us who are either directly involved in the energy field or have a considerable interest in it, have a responsibility, I believe, to inform those responsible for planning, policy and decision taking about what the facts are and what measures need to be taken if these crises, both the short and medium term, and the long term, are going to be avoided. That this is a matter of deep interest is evidenced by the fact that The Times, very recently, started a series of three articles on this very subject. The Daily Telegraph this morning has its first lead article on the question of oil supplies, but

1

fortunately, I see, it reaches the conclusion that we are not in a situation of crisis, but that we have to take serious thought as to how the next few years are to be coped with.

May I just say one other thing about the appropriateness of our discussing the subject at this vital time. One of the most essential component parts of our energy situation at the moment is the situation in the United States of America. As you will all have seen from your programme, very unfortunately Charles Zraket of the Mitre Corporation who was scheduled to talk on the US situation had to withdraw at the very last moment. It was with very great regret that he withdrew. However, when he *was* coming here, he was going to fly direct from Tokyo to London in order to take part in this conference and deliver his paper, which I think was a measure of the importance that he felt this subject deserved and that this audience commanded. When Charles Zraket withdrew we invited and got an acceptance from Jim Akins, who was originally responsible for drafting President Nixon's energy message, to take part in this conference and deliver a paper, an invitation that he very happily took up if he was going to be free. It was also his intention to be present throughout the entire three days of the meeting. However, very unfortunately, at the last moment he had to withdraw and we are very fortunate that John Lichtblau of PIRINC will be coming at the end of the week to talk to us on the USA. Nevertheless, I think this is a token of the importance that people within the USA consider this topic, and recognise that this is not just an American problem, but one of world-wide significance.

Before I hand over to Colin Maynard who has a few administrative details to put over to you, may I express my gratitude at this stage to the very considerable help I have had, not only from people who are here today, but also from some who unfortunately are not able to be present at the Summer Meeting. May I do that as a blanket thanks.

But I would like to express special thanks to Ted Newland who is co-author, as you will see, of one of the papers, was on the committee which organised this Summer Meeting and whose brainchild this meeting and its topic was. To a very great extent it was his imagination and sense of timing that enabled us to hold the conference at this vital time.

CHAPTER 1

Energy: The Changed and Changing Scene

GEOFFREY CHANDLER

President of the Institute of Petroleum

World energy resources, allied to the development of technology, should in the long term provide sufficient energy to meet world needs. In the shorter term there appears the possibility of scarcity*—the first in peacetime industrial history apart from emergency situations—if no action is taken to prevent it. This possibility derives not from lack of energy reserves, but from the political and economic implications of the relationship between world demand and the current pattern of reserves and from the long lead time required to develop alternatives. This paper analyses the factors underlying this changed situation and suggests policy measures to meet it.

The postwar energy scene has been marked by strength of demand and abundance of supply. It has seen the change from a coal to an oil age, the rapid emergence of natural gas, and the slow introduction of nuclear power (Fig. 1).

The abundant availability of oil, its convenience, and its lower price (Fig. 2) led to substitution of coal by oil and in general a buyer's market for energy. Energy policies in consuming countries—in so far as they existed beyond a rationalisation of letting competition work and obtaining energy at the lowest possible cost—were generally designed to give protection to coal, while the taxman exploited the price inelasticity of demand for gasoline. For the greater part of this period oil production capacity was greater than demand, providing flexibility of supply in times of climatic, operational, or political difficulty, and diminishing the producing countries' opportunity to secure a significantly higher tax take. Many of these factors are still recognisable in the energy scene today.

The pace of demand, ignoring fluctuations round the trend, appears as

---

* The phrase 'energy crisis' has become a popular means of describing this situation, though it has been used less by writers knowledgeable in the energy field than by academics and journalists anxious to point a moral, adorn a tale, or provide an Aunt Sally with which to bolster a prejudice. I use the word 'scarcity' to describe a situation in which normal demand under normal conditions cannot be satisfied on a continuing basis by available supply and in which economic forces have insufficient time to recreate a balance without unacceptable discomfort.

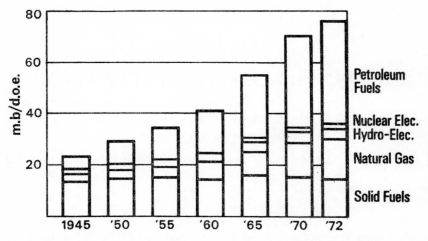

FIG. 1. World commercial energy demand 1945–1972 (excluding USSR, China and
E. Europe).

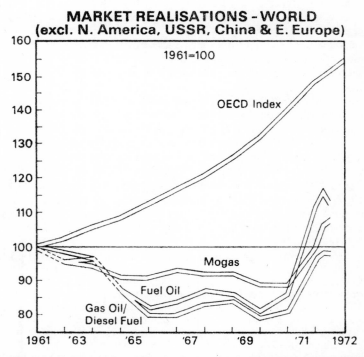

FIG. 2. Price trends for main products (excluding duties and taxes) with the **OECD GNP**
deflation index as a crude indicator of general price inflation.

strong as ever (Fig. 3) and no energy paper would be complete without an eyebrow lifted at the grosser infelicities of earlier forecasters (Fig. 4). The purpose of this diagram, however, is not to mock those who fell into what has proved almost universal error, but to illustrate the persistent tendency to underestimate the strength of demand in a situation where no positive measures are taken to control its rate of expansion and no negative factors exist to inhibit its continued exponential growth.

Substitution of coal by oil has diminished, but oil continues to be the chief contributor to incremental supply world-wide, though its pace of growth, as it acquires a larger share of total supply, is moving closer to that of energy as a whole.

The underlying reserve position appears at first glance still to be a strong one, although various restrictions on production in the first half of 1973 may have temporarily obscured this, and increasing strength of demand for certain quality crudes may tend to sustain an impression of continuing difficulty. Nonetheless the energy climate has radically changed, even if more in prospect than in actuality.

The oil industry has traditionally forecast oil demand by estimating the supply of other fuels and assuming that oil would fill the resultant gap. When other fuels have fallen short of their targets (as has often been the case) oil has been able to expand to take their place. Today we can no longer look to 'gapology' as a valid technique of forecasting, and the comfort to be derived from familiar charts (Fig. 5) may well be illusory. The change lies partly in the pattern of demand, but more fundamentally in the pattern of supply.

The change in demand lies not in any alteration of the pace of growth but in a significant increase in the demand for imported energy (Fig. 6). The new factor here is the widening gap between domestic supply and demand in the USA as a result of the diminishing availability of natural gas, the peaking out of oil production (excluding Alaska's potential), and environmental pressures against the development of new oil, coal, or nuclear resources. The USA will now therefore join Western Europe and Japan as a major importer of oil, calling on the main world source of incremental oil, the Middle East. And it is therefore the level of reserves and their geographical location which are the critical determinants of the immediate future, since the lead time required to bring about any significant alteration to the energy scene may be as much as 10 to 15 years, and even this could only be achieved if action were initiated with urgency.

It is in the pattern of supply and the factors that may affect it that more fundamental changes have come about. In contemplating the more distant energy scene I believe it has in the past been reasonable to visualise the gradual flattening and then reduction of oil demand in percentage and, ultimately, in absolute terms as nuclear power increasingly entered the scene. It was a matter of taste (or of subjective bias) whether such a change was placed around the year 2000, or earlier, or later. Such a view was founded on the concept of an orderly progression in which reserves would be produced in response to demand and economics would act as the natural arbiter between the various sources of supply and their end uses. Today I believe that the time-span available to us may be relatively short and that positive efforts must be made to ensure that such an ordered progression comes about.

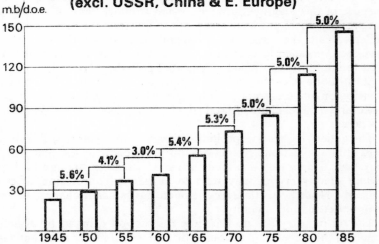

FIG. 3.   Energy growth rates by 5-year intervals. The forecast is based on a 'surprise-free' scenario and is intended to illustrate the strength of demand under 'normal' conditions.

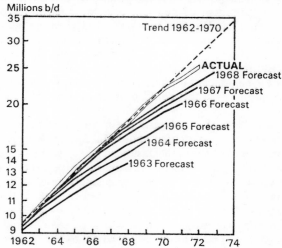

FIG. 4.   The familiar forecaster's 'horse's tail'. Forecasting of oil product demand has historically underestimated the actual increase of demand. Total energy forecasts have understandably shown less variance.

WORLD COMMERCIAL ENERGY DEMAND 1972-1985
(excl. USSR, China & E. Europe)

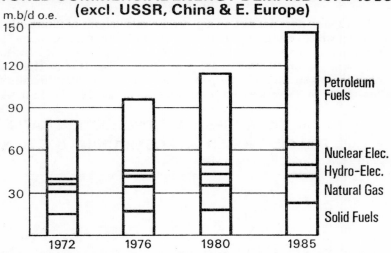

m.b/d o.e.

Petroleum Fuels

Nuclear Elec.
Hydro-Elec.
Natural Gas
Solid Fuels

FIG. 5. A possible 'surprise-free' projection of energy demand and supply to 1985. Over this time period it is important to emphasise the relative inelasticity of nuclear power.

GROWTH OF OIL IMPORTS (mb/d)

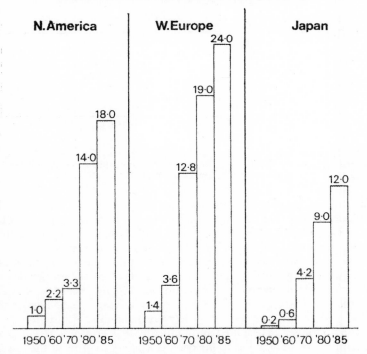

FIG. 6. There is a significant range of uncertainty underlying future estimates. The time up to 1980, however, is probably insufficient to allow marked change to improve requirements and this year is therefore emphasised. Russia is assumed neither to have a significant requirement for imports nor to be a significant contributor to supply over this period.

Such a view does not rest on any precise calculations of future oil supply or demand, which, except in extreme scenarios of prolonged economic recession or exceptional growth, I believe to be largely irrelevant to the issue.

Current proven oil reserves are in principle sufficient to meet demand until other sources of oil and energy can begin to make a contribution (Fig. 7). Two-thirds of these are, however, located in the Middle East. And it is

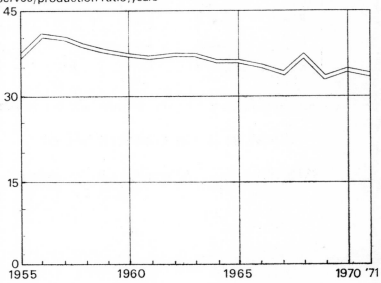

INDUSTRY RESERVES/PRODUCTION RATIO
FOR OIL-WORLD (excl. USSR, CHINA & E. Europe)

FIG. 7.   The above ratios have been derived from estimates of reserves and production data, published annually by 'World Oil'. The high R/P ratio in 1968 reflects a substantial upward revision of the reserves estimate for Saudi Arabia.

today the geography of reserves, not their quantum, which is the most significant aspect. They are technically capable of very high levels of production (Figs. 8 and 9), though their price is likely to be determined by relative bargaining power, enhanced by quasi-monopoly postures, not by potential availability. Such levels, however, assume that the rate of production required by the consuming areas is similar to that required by the economic and social needs of the economies of the host countries. It is this assumption, quite apart from the strategic considerations inherent in relying on one part of the world for the greater part of energy supply, that demands examination.

It can no longer be assumed automatically that production will grow at the rate required by demand as in the past. It is likely to grow at the rate required by the long-term economic needs of the countries in which the oil resource originates. Two factors suggest that this may not be as fast as demand requires unless positive measures are taken to mitigate them.

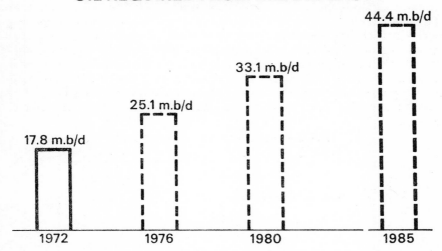

OIL REQUIRED FROM MIDDLE EAST

FIG. 8.   Estimates for future, broadly consistent with assumptions underlying Fig. 6, again subject to wide variation.

POSSIBLE PRODUCTION LEVELS

(MILLIONS B/D)

Year	S. Arabia	Iran	Iraq	Kuwait	Abu Dhabi
1973	6.6	5.6	1.8	3.3	1.2
1976	10	8	3	3.5	2.5
1980	14	9	5	3.5	4.5
1985	23	10	8	3.5	5.5

Year	Qatar	Libya	Nigeria	Venezuela	Indonesia
1973	0.5	2.2	2.0	3.3	1.4
1976	0.5	2.5	2.5	3.4	2.0
1980	0.5	3	3	2.5	2.5
1985	0.5	2.5	3	2.5	3

FIG. 9.   Theoretical production levels physically obtainable on present assumptions on reserves.

The first is the probable desire of many producing countries to work towards an 'optimum' reserve/production ratio which takes into account the fact that petroleum is their main or sole resource. There is of course a strong incentive for countries with large populations and corresponding development needs to generate finance for development through the sale of oil. But economies dependent on a single commodity are not easily diversified and those countries which have relatively limited reserves may consider it appropriate to prorate production at a pace which ensures a longer life for their existing oilfields (Fig. 10). There are others with smaller populations and large reserves

IRAN - Reserves vs. Production

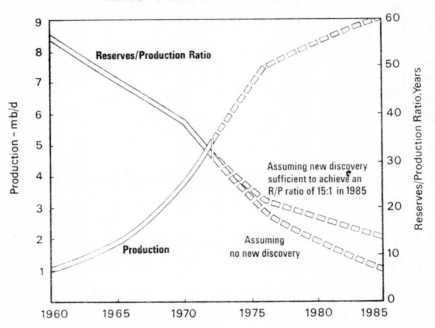

FIG. 10.   An illustration of the interaction of production levels and the reserve/production ratio for a given country. Future estimates are no more than illustrative of the way in which such an interaction can develop. A decrease in the rate of production would have an effect on the R/P ratio comparable to an increase in reserves.

which may find that the generation of money from the sale of oil is larger than the most optimistic assumptions of absorptive capacity can deal with (Figs. 11 and 12).

Finance is only one input to development, and the absorption capacity of an economy may be limited by several factors such as infrastructure, education, or human resources. The sums of money that may be surplus to domestic requirements could reach a magnitude that would pose new problems to the international monetary system and would require new mechanisms if such money is to be absorbed usefully from the producing country's point of view and benignly from the point of view of the rest of the world.

The problems inherent in such a situation should not be beyond the wit of man to solve. But to do so calls for positive policies and a degree of international co-operation which is not easily achieved except in times of emergency. Assistance in the diversification of producing country economies, investment in refining and in chemical plant 'upstream' rather than in the markets, the absorption of funds by investment in industrialised economies,

ESTIMATED PRODUCTION AND REVENUE

		Production m b/d	Revenue $/Bn
1975	Middle East	25.3	16
	North Africa	3.4	3.1
	Total	28.7	19.1
1980	Middle East	45.0	58
	North Africa	3.5	5.4
	Total	48.5	63.4

1975 — average tax take (Tehran agreement)
$1.80 per bbl unadjusted for currency changes.

1980 — average tax take $3.50 bbl Middle East;
$4.25 North Africa.

(Source: James Akins)

FIG. 11. A wide variety of estimates could be given for tax takes in 1980. These estimates, given by the former energy adviser to the White House (*Foreign Affairs*, 1(3), 1973), may well be conservative, but are sufficient to illustrate the very large sums of money which may be generated and which may find problems in being absorbed in the world economy unless thought is given to the matter. Other observers of the scene have suggested tax takes twice as high. A do-it-yourself calculation on preferred rates of take can be simply undertaken.

and aid to developing countries are all theoretical outlets for financial sums of a size the world has not before experienced. Participation in world financial councils by the generators of this wealth will also be a clear necessity.

For consuming countries the policies which are appropriate to this situation spring logically from the diagnosis.

In the immediate context there is a need for restraint. For those who lack indigenous energy supplies or the prospect of them, or who gain nothing from the existing structure of the industry, there is an obvious temptation to try and buy a position which will protect them in the event of shortage. Such action, however, will do nothing to increase total resources: it may simply bid up prices, put strain on agreements which are reached with the producing countries, and perhaps induce the shortage it is intended to prevent, since the closer balance of current demand and supply potential today means that disruptions—from whatever cause—cannot be overcome with the flexibility of the past. Some form of agreement that available supplies will be fairly shared in the event of shortage therefore seems urgently necessary.

Emergency storage and rationing schemes as a defence against any emergency through the partial denial of oil such as has been experienced in the past would also be sensible policies to adopt. These solve no resource problems, but could provide a breathing space in which to find political solutions to political problems. I do not believe that such consumer co-operation should be intended, or interpreted, as confrontation. The avoidance of disruption in a market is normally welcome to producers and consumers alike.

THE MAJOR OIL EXPORTERS

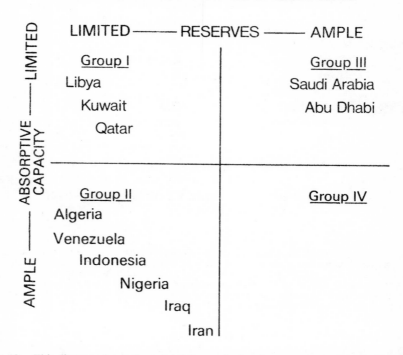

FIG. 12.   This diagram shows the potential capacity for the generation of money (reserves on present assumptions) and the apparent capacity to absorb such financial resources (absorptive capacity). It poses a problem which may require solution; it does not imply it is insoluble.

Agreement to share supplies if necessary is a measure which could have effect in the short term. The basic problem, however, of adequacy of supply will only be resolved by the creation of new resources and the tempering of the rate of increase of demand—both of which have long lead times.

For the longer term there is need to shift the geography of reserves by intensifying the search for oil in new areas, to lay the foundations for the post-oil age by the further development of coal and the promotion of nuclear energy, and to reduce the inefficiency and wastage inherent in energy use today. Increasing cost may help towards the last, but experience shows that this is probably insufficient as a spur and that more systematic measures may have to be taken to reduce the rate of growth of demand, for example by rationalising transport, by improving insulation standards, by the selective use of fuels in their more efficient applications. There is a long lead time to the fulfilment of all these aims, and action therefore requires to be initiated with the utmost urgency.

In addition there is need for consultation between the producers and the consumers, among which the consumers of the developing world must be included, in order to find some solution to the problems inherent in the present situation. The possession of vital materials by countries otherwise poor and in many cases underdeveloped, who thus have the prospect of great riches, should be a recipe in any sensible world for creative good. The world we live in may not justify such optimism, and it may be that the best we can hope for is an attempt to muddle through to an age in which some of the obvious needs in the energy field are brought about not by forethought but through discomfort and belated necessity. The past two winters in the United Kingdom, when coal, gas, and electricity have been sporadically denied through industrial action, and the present energy discontents of the United States—both springing from causes basically unrelated to the underlying energy supply/demand situation—may unhappily prove to have been good practice for the future.

I would nonetheless hope we can do better than this, and there is a real choice before us today—either to use the time still available for constructive

TOTAL WORLD ENERGY CONSUMPTION
AND RESOURCES IN YEAR 2000

World consumption 1972 ....5.5×10^9 oil equivalent tons

Estimated world consumption in 2000 ....25×10^9 oil equivalent tons

Reserves	Tons Oil Equivalent	Times Year 2000 Consumption
Fossil fuels		
Ultimate reserves of coal, oil, gas, shale, tar sands recoverable with high technology	5×10^{12}	200
Nuclear		
Total fission fuel if used in current reactors (10 million tons of U_3O_8)	0.1×10^{12}	4
Total fission with breeder reactors	15×10^{12}	600
Nuclear fusion (conversion of all ocean Deuterium)	$35,000 \times 10^{12}$	1½ million
Other resources		
World solar input	125×10^{12}	5000
Potential useful hydropower	25×10^8	1/10th
Useful geothermal flow	1×10^8	1/250th
Usable tidal energy	0.5×10^8	1/5000th

FIG. 13. An attempt to illustrate the potential energy resource picture in the year 2000. 'Other resources' are not comparable with the two preceding categories, being 'income' as opposed to 'capital'. The reserve/production figure for nuclear fusion is probably greatly underrated, but the understatement does not diminish a picture of abundance. Technology is assumed, but may well be premature for the newer sources of energy.

planning on an international plane, or to let slip an opportunity which may not come again.

The long-term energy reserve situation (Fig. 13) provides assurance that given the finance (the requirements for which will be very large indeed), given the technology, and—what is most important—given the time, there should be no anxiety. But to reach without intervening scarcity the point at which these can be mobilised will require statesmanship, forethought, and urgent action. There are other aspects which I have not touched on in this paper such as the potential impact of the changing energy scene on national balances of payments, especially in developing countries, and the changing relationship of energy to gross national product. These too require study.

In none of this is it possible to make forecasts either of timing or of quantity which are not subject to wide margins. There is clearly a danger that the will to act could be sapped if a buyer's market in energy, which could indeed be compatible with the immediate reserve/demand situation, were to re-emerge.

The only prediction I would make with confidence is that if the time we still have left is not used for positive action, when that action is finally seen to be necessary because shortage is upon us it will then be too late to avert a problem of major proportions.

Discussion

Professor P. R. Odell (Erasmus University, Rotterdam): Why in the presentation is the scenario established for a supply crisis? Why will there be no consumer reaction in terms of the development of demand to the kinds of prices which must emerge from the tax tables mentioned (*e.g.* $7/brl, *i.e.* 2 × Akins figure of $3.50 by 1980)? Is the system no longer self-adjusting in any respect?

Why do we ignore the *existing* developments of alternative oil/energy supplies already emerging out of, for example (a) Western Europe's ability to produce oil and gas in quantities which *could* (given the full co-operation of the oil companies concerned) limit the area's 1980 oil import requirements to the 1970 level. (b) The ability and *will* of the US to minimise its oil import needs even in this decade. (c) The revised Japanese expectations of a very significant fall in energy growth demand rates—and hence in rates of increase in oil imports?

On the basis of a set of the worst possible assumptions about the next 10 years, the President has succeeded in talking us—and others—into accepting the idea of the inevitability of a crisis.

Mr G. Chandler: The whole burden of my thesis is that a crisis is avoidable, but that it requires an unbiased understanding of the possibilities inherent in the changed supply and demand situation if the right measures to avoid it are to be adopted. My assumptions sit somewhere in the middle of the range of possibilities and are neither 'best' nor 'worst'. Prices—if they are allowed by governments to respond to market forces—may in some measure moderate demand, though historically demand has shown little elasticity in relation to price and the lead time for significant impact, involving as it does changes in established industrial and social behaviour, is likely to be long. The full oil and gas potential of Western Europe is only likely to be realised if policy-makers are aware of the need for it: its quantum of course remains unknown. Unsubstantiated optimism may dull the necessary awareness and weaken the resolve to see this potential developed.

15

CHAPTER 2

The Prospects for Coal

D. H. BROADBENT

Director of Special Projects, National Coal Board, London, UK

INTRODUCTION

I am delighted to attend the 1973 Summer Meeting of the Institute of Petroleum, particularly in view of the wide-ranging nature of the meeting which covers all of the major energy industries. Indeed, as I look down the programme and see the number of eminent men discussing what I consider to be the major energy problems facing us today, I cannot recall seeing such a well balanced programme at one conference, and I must congratulate the organisers of the Meeting on their ability in drawing up the programme.

It has been a theme of mine for some time now that energy is so fundamental to our economic existence that the idea of any of the energy industries being mutually exclusive is totally unrealistic. Of course, market pressures, strategic thinking and socio-economic pressures will decide the share of the energy market, but at the end of the day we will need all of our energy industries and resources ideally integrated yet remaining in economic contention. I look forward to seeing how this theme will develop during the next three days of this Summer Meeting.

In my paper I will set out how coal will fit into the energy picture in the next twelve years and perhaps look a little further ahead to see how our present research work in the Coal Industry may come to fruition in perhaps a further ten years or so. I will first of all deal very briefly with the world energy scene and the role of coal as a major hydrocarbon source. I will then consider how the Coal Industry may develop in the next few years and how the mining techniques and markets for coal and coal products may change to suit the changing energy markets in the future. I will finish by giving some of our ideas, which are currently at the research stage, but which could radically change the Coal Industry from that which we know today.

WORLD ENERGY SCENE

I will not spell out in detail the problem of whether the world growth in energy demand can be met from present indigenous resources, as I am sure that everybody present at this assembly has heard of the 'energy gap' theory and the possible energy crisis looming up on the horizon. I think it suffices

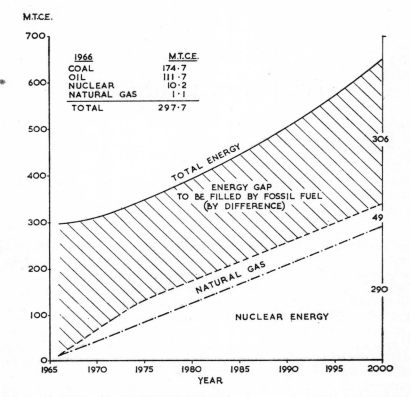

FIG. 1.   Projection showing the total fossil fuel energy gap up to the year 2000 (UK).

to restate in simple terms that on present trends, even with a successful nuclear industry providing 90 % of our electricity, by the end of the century there will still be more fossil fuel needed than today (Fig. 1).

The simple question is therefore—can the growing demand for fossil fuel continue to be met, largely by the oil industry? I would refer you to some current and authoritative statements on this simple question:

(i) F. S. McFadzean, Chairman of the Shell Transport & Trading Company, in his foreword to the Annual Report for 1972 stated 'At present oil and gas provide between them more than 70 % of world energy consumption. By 1985, when energy consumption is expected to have doubled, that percentage is likely to be much the same; no alternative energy source can be developed in time to make a sizeable impact. . . . Oil companies will continue to provide the base load but this cannot be done without tapping new sources far more expensive than those currently available'.

(ii) Mr Henri Simonet, the Common Market Commissioner for Energy, in May of this year outlined proposals for an energy policy in Europe aimed at reducing dependence on the Middle East for oil imports. The policy would be based on an expanded nuclear programme and full use of indigenous coal resources coupled with co-operation in research between the USA, Japan and Europe and the avoidance of 'useless and costly over-bidding for crude oil amongst the major consuming powers'.

(iii) Sir Eric Drake, Chairman of BP Ltd, also said in May of this year that 'For the years ahead it is clear that oil cannot be relied upon automatically to cover any energy shortfall, as it has done in recent years'.

The future energy scene is therefore one of tightening supplies and increased costs and, on an international basis, the political implications of energy supply will become of major importance. General George Lincoln, until recently Director of the United States Office of Emergency Preparedness, went so far as to say in December of last year 'The big debate on energy is going to continue. In my opinion it is going to replace the cold war as the most urgent problem facing America in the years ahead'.

Consider the position of coal against this background.

COAL INDUSTRY

Coal comprises some 93% of the world's fossil fuel reserves. In the UK we are particularly fortunate in that our proved reserves of coal could sustain the present level of output for 100 years or more—if access to those reserves is maintained. It is this factor that has led to a £3 million borehole drilling programme for the next 2 years recently mounted by the Board to locate precisely the position of the coal, to determine the quality of the coal and the best mining techniques for its extraction.

Let us consider the economics of coal mining in this country. In the 1960s, the mechanisation of coalface operations was virtually completed—and in that period productivity increased from about 28 cwt/manshift to 43 cwt. Productivity is now running at record levels of over 48 cwt/manshift and is rising.

It is sometimes thought that because mechanised face equipment is now practically completed the prospects for further increases in productivity are marginal. This is not the case; I recently visited one of the more modern collieries where productivity is over twice the national average, using the same equipment and technology as in other pits. A feature of this pit is that the mine was designed as a whole where the coal handling and preparation equipment were matched to the coal cutting machinery, rather than installing modern equipment in old mines, as has happened so often in the past.

The fact is that there has been no net investment in the Coal Industry for the last decade in that investment has been less than depreciation. There is no doubt in my mind that the potential for cheap coal exists, using present technology, but with sufficient investment to ensure that the system is designed as a whole.

The 'cross-over' point between the price of coal and that of oil will, of course, be the major stimulus for a re-appraisal of the economics of coal and the level of investment and research in coal. The Board already has plans for integrating existing mines for large multi-million ton coal complexes, designed for specific markets with the minimum of coal preparation, to suit merry-go-round trains to get the coal to the customer at the lowest possible cost. One must bear in mind that for years the Coal Industry has been run down, even on an international level, but the situation has now changed radically and we are witnessing some exciting prospects for coal, particularly in the USA where it is planned to double the output of the Coal Industry in the next twelve years.

The mining techniques of the future will essentially be associated with the markets of the future and the $2 billion dollar programme for coal development proposed by Carl E. Bagge in the UK last month sets out some ideas for coal, including gasification of coal, liquefaction of coal and the use of coal for chemical feedstocks and also for power generation. The role of coal as a hydrocarbon source of synthetic fuels is confirmed by the USA Petroleum Council Report of 1972 which predicts up to 339 million tons of coal a year going to make synthetic fuels by 1985.

The exact route which coal will take in the next few years as a support for conventional liquid and gaseous fuels is discussed in detail in the next section. What is certain, however, is that these new techniques are relatively insensitive to the normal coal quality in terms of ash content, ash type, moisture and fines, etc. Mining technology could therefore be revolutionised compared with that existing today where most of the skills and expertise have basically gone into producing a coal which is cheap to transport and easy to burn.

Coal ash or residue was once regarded as a waste product. We are now beginning to realise that this material represents a valuable mineral asset. It has pozzolanic properties and is ideal material for bulk structural applications, building materials, and the production of synthetic aggregates. Tests on suitably treated materials have shown it to have good non-skid properties for road surfacing—a potential market of around 50 million tons a year.

It is the market value of coal as a hydrocarbon and mineral resource that will dictate mining techniques of the future. These should lead to more automatic mining, fewer problems with ash quality and a new degree of freedom for mining research, including possibly hydraulic mining and transport. If, in the future, a fraction of the research effort and university graduate man-hours goes into mining research which has gone into nuclear R & D, then we could perhaps have a mining industry in the future which is vastly different from today.

FUTURE DEVELOPMENTS

In the future we envisage that coal, oil shales and tar sands will be used to supplement the natural sources of oil and gas. The exact timing of these developments is difficult to predict on economic grounds and in any event may be forestalled by strategic or political considerations.

Gasification of coal is, of course, proven technology for low Btu gas and in the USA serious consideration is being given to production of low Btu gas to provide a low-sulphur fuel for mine-mouth power plants. To produce synthetic natural gas requires some technological development. At the

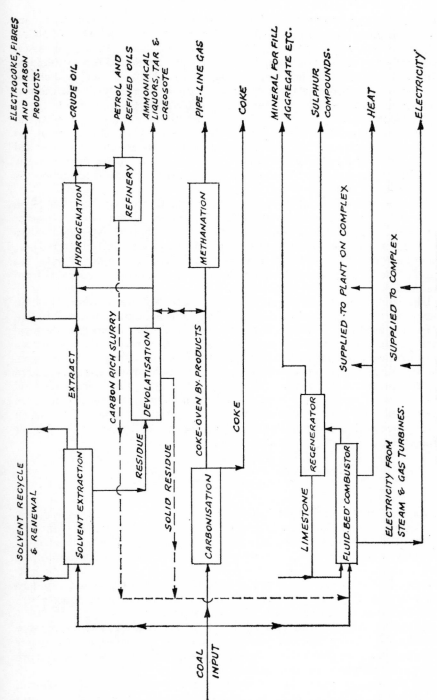

FIG. 2. Possible outline scheme for COALPLEX.

Westfield site, now producing 'town gas', an American oil company consortium is planning a programme in the £m range for production of SNG.

The NCB is also carrying out research in this field and the process is essentially a pyrolysis/hydrogenation process using fluidised bed technology. Fluidised beds are eminently suited to this process, both as an efficient chemical reactor and also as a low temperature combustion system which allows combustion to take place with virtually no emission of sulphur oxides.

The Board has a world lead in fluidised bed technology and is carrying out contract work in the million dollar range for the USA Government and industrial interests and also for oil companies in this country. The fluidised bed technology for direct production of power is now being commercially exploited by a company known as Combustion Systems Ltd under the auspices of the NRDC.

Another area of useful work is in the production of synthetic crude oil from coal digests. Liquid solvents such as anthracene oil are used. One rather novel technique being developed at our Coal Research Establishment involves using gas at super-critical pressures (*e.g.* toluene at around 100 atm). These gases have the advantage that they dissolve the coal in the liquid state, but upon reducing the pressure the gaseous coal solution is easily separated from the insoluble char and mineral matter.

Ultimately we envisage that this basic work will form elements of an integrated plant known as the COALPLEX, shown diagrammatically in Fig. 2. Coal is used as a feedstock for producing synthetic oil and gas, chemical feedstocks and coke products, and the energy for the process. The production of synthetic oil and gas from coal is achieved essentially by adding hydrogen. On the other hand, crude oil contains rather more hydrogen than is required for the present day product mix—particularly with the more recent oil discoveries of lighter oils. It is possible therefore to envisage a complex where coal is solvent extracted and the extract mixed with crude oil to form a homogeneous liquid containing the right amount of hydrogen for further processing.

CONCLUSION

In conclusion, I believe that by 1985 we will see a coal mining industry developing to suit the hydrocarbon and energy market, rather than as a source of crude heat. I can envisage plants being developed on the lines of the Coalplex concept—almost certainly with the USA taking the technological lead.

These developments must have a considerable impact on mining techniques and coal handling and coal preparation, so that the mining industry will probably be quite different from what we have today.

Returning to my introductory point, I believe that we will see a more co-ordinated energy industry with joint coal/oil, gas and nuclear plants operating in a complementary way to provide the energy resources which are vital to our economic development of the future.

The NCB see energy and environmental problems as being indivisible and of interest to all energy industries and is willing to co-operate on a joint

Research and Development programme with any interested parties. This applies to co-operation in the United Kingdom, in Europe or on an international basis with other countries such as the USA or Japan.

(*The discussion for this chapter is on page* 37.)

CHAPTER 3

Future Petroleum Supplies—Onshore and Offshore

T. F. GASKELL

British Petroleum Co. Ltd, London, UK

WORLD RESOURCES OF OIL

Formation of oil

Petroleum, natural gas and coal exist in finite quantities in the earth since all are fossil fuels, laid down millions of years ago. Coal and oil stocks are not replaceable in the time span in which human activity is counted.

Crude oil, consisting of a mixture of hydrocarbons ranging from the gas methane (CH_4) through liquids consisting of various more complex molecules to solids such as waxes and bitumen, has its origin in decaying plant and animal life. Petroleum is associated with sedimentary rocks, since the decay of plant and animal material took place in shallow water marine conditions. At the beginning of the oil cycle about 200 parts of oil were associated with a million parts of sea water, and in order to form a reservoir of oil that is economic to produce, a concentration of the oil must have taken place. This process is probably governed by gravity forces, and oil accumulations are normally found in porous limestone or sandstone rocks, with the lighter petroleum floating on top of salt water. Some form of trap, such as an anticlinal fold in the rock strata, is needed to allow the oil to collect separately from the water. In order to keep the oil accumulation from leaking to the surface an impervious layer of cap-rock is a further requirement in order to produce an economic oil field.

Because there are several necessary conditions for oil accumulation—thick marine sediments, porous reservoir rock, some form of geological trap and an adequate cap-rock—oil fields of a size to be economic to produce form a small fraction of the area of a sedimentary basin. For example, in the North Sea, where there are 200 000 square miles of sediments, there may be ten or twenty oil or gas fields of areas averaging about 40 square miles. On a volume basis, since the porosity of the reservoir rock ranges from say 5–20 % of the rock volume, the oil in a sedimentary basin occupies only about one part in 50 000 of the volume of sediments.

Proved reserves

Since economic oil concentrations are only found in comparatively small structures in sedimentary basins, it is difficult to estimate what volume of oil exists below ground without locating the oil fields and drilling many holes in order to evaluate the size of the reservoir. In this respect estimation of the total oil existing in the world is more difficult than is calculating coal reserves. Coal being a solid is laid down in strata which can often be followed from surface outcrop to depths which are economically mineable. Geological reasoning, together with well placed test boreholes, can delineate large areas of coal deposits in a way that is not possible for petroleum.

Since it is expensive to drill an oil field sufficiently to estimate the amount of oil in place, and since an oil field that is drilled up and is not producing is providing no return on capital expended, it is the practice in the industry to move to production as soon as possible. Oil fields are planned to have a finite life of the order of 20 years or more—a time which bears some relation to the life of steel structural materials, to good reservoir operating techniques and to an ultimate offtake rate which is economic to work. Therefore the oil reserves which are known for certain, and which are based on fields already discovered, almost automatically are about 15 or 20 times current production rates.

The published 'proved' oil reserves at the end of 1972[1] were 91 000 million tons (673 × 10⁹ brl) of which more than half is in the Middle East. The world production for 1972 was about 2600 million tons, so that at that time world reserves were good for 35 years. It may well be that the 1972 figures provide a longer certain look ahead in reserves for the industry than will occur at any time in the future, since the rate of increase of demand continues to be very rapid.

Ultimate reserves

Many geologists and reservoir engineers have made estimates of the total reserves in the world of conventional crude oil. A good summary of these is given in Table 1, taken from an excellent paper by H. R. Warman 'The Future of Oil'.[2] It is interesting, and perhaps encouraging, at least to the optimists in the industry, to note the increase in estimates by a factor of four that have taken place during the past thirty years. However, during the past decade, the numbers have settled down at around 2000 × 10⁹ brl—or about 300 000 million tons, and it is probable that this represents a good estimate that will not change much in future. This is because, during the past 25 years, extensive exploration in many parts of the world has taken place, and geophysics and drilling have probed structures to the 10 000 to 20 000 ft depths below which economic oil accumulations do not appear to exist.

The estimates of total world oil are made in several ways. One can extrapolate from sedimentary areas which have been thoroughly well prospected and drilled, and the oil per square mile of sedimentary basin can be assumed to be the same for other parts of the world. A similar calculation may be made on a volume basis, by determining a figure for the average oil per cubic mile of sedimentary rock. A more detailed survey takes into account the geological idiosyncracies of each sedimentary basin, and allows estimates to be made individually for all potentially productive areas of the world. Table 1 demonstrates that, allowing for a large uncertainty, there is a good measure of agreement at around 300 000 million tons of liquid hydrocarbons for the world to use.

TABLE 1
**Estimates of World Ultimate Reserves of Crude Oil From
Conventional Sources**

Year	Source	$\times 10^9$ brl
1942	Pratt, Weeks and Stebinger	600
1946	Duce	400
1946	Pogue	555
1948	Weeks	610
1949	Levorsen	1 500
1949	Weeks	1 010
1953	MacNaughton	1 000
1956	Hubbert	1 250
1958	Weeks	1 500
1959	Weeks	2 000
1965	Hendricks (USGS)	2 480
1967	Ryman (Esso)	2 090
1968	Shell	1 800
1968	Weeks	2 200
1969	Hubbert	1 350–2 100
1970	Moody (Mobil)	1 800
1971	Warman (BP)	1 200–2 000
1971	Weeks	2 290

Figure 1 (after Warman[2]) shows the proved and undiscovered oil as at 1971. It is interesting to see that although the Middle East holds the largest reserves in the world most of it has already been found, so its long-term potential may decline.

Offshore oil
Following work by marine geophysicists thirty to forty years ago, it was realised that the shallow continental shelves which fringe the land were, from a geological standpoint, part of the land pattern, although the true deep ocean, where the sea is 4–5 km deep, is a separate geological province. If oil accumulations are found on land, therefore, it was to be assumed that similar oil fields existed offshore on the shelves adjacent to land. It is estimated today that one quarter of the world's oil is to be found on the shallow continental shelves. An interesting paper by Weeks[3] combines the continental shelf with the land coastal plains, since they are generally part of the same topographic (and geological) feature. This part of the earth is estimated to hold over 75% of the world's oil.

Gas reserves
The North Sea provides some interesting lessons for the oil explorer. In the southern half of the sedimentary basin some large gas fields have been discovered. The geological picture continues from the Groningen gas field in Holland across the North Sea to Yorkshire, and it is not surprising to find fields similar to Groningen in between the two land areas. However, the gas, which is almost pure methane, has its origin in the Coal Measures, laid

down over 300 million years ago, and not in decaying marine animals, which is the normal source of petroleum. The methane from the fresh water deposits of coal leaked upwards into a thick porous sandstone reservoir in the Basal Permian Series.

In the northern region of the North Sea basin, true marine origin oil and associated gas has been discovered at Forties, Ekofisk and other fields. An interesting geological point here is that the oil fields are in a thick sedimentary basin lying between the igneous rocks of Scotland and Norway. This is a case where one does not blindly follow the land geology out to the continental shelf, since the coastline coincides with a geological discontinuity. It had been known for a long time to geologists that sediments had been accumulating between Scotland and Norway for over 100 million years, but the example does serve to remind one that care must be taken to watch for exceptions to general rules.

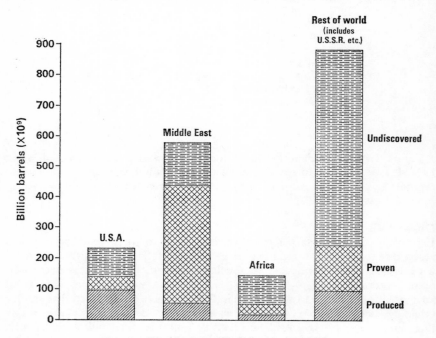

FIG. 1.   World crude oil balance sheet in 1971.

Oil fields are often saturated with gas at the pressure corresponding to the hydrostatic head for the depth of the field. Thus, in the convenient ft/lb/sec system of units, the pressure of gas in an oil reservoir in lb/sq inch is half the depth in feet. There are exceptions, since some fields exist in which the oil is undersaturated with gas, while in others movement of semi-fluid rocks such as salt may cause oversaturation of gas. In oil fields at depths of 10 000 ft the weight of gas associated with oil may be as much as a quarter of the weight of the crude oil in the reservoir. The Ekofisk field is oversaturated and the amount of energy in the gas produced in the next 20 years may well exceed that of the oil.

Figure 2 (from Warman)[2] shows that the total natural gas reserves, adding the associated gas to plain gas field reserves, is almost equal in barrels of oil equivalent to the crude oil reserves. Both are considerably less than the reserves of solid fuels. This is not surprising, for apart from the complicated process of accumulating oil and gas, being fluids they tend to leak upwards and get lost at the surface of the earth, whereas coal and shale, being solids,

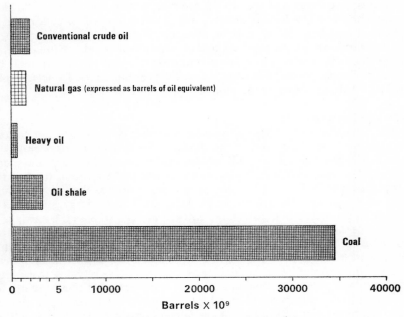

FIG. 2.   World oil sources and natural gas.

stay put even when the rock strata are badly fractured and disturbed. The fact that oil and gas are fluids makes them much easier to extract and handle than coal or shale, and so accounts for their ascendency in the energy world of today. It is to be expected that discoveries of natural gas will keep pace with those of oil in the future. There is a tendency for oil to be produced from deeper reservoirs than in the past, and hence on average to have a higher gas/oil ratio. Furthermore, very deep drilling may find gas alone at depths which are too hot for oil fields. However, recent boreholes to 30 000 ft in the USA have been disappointing in the search for gas. It must be realised that the gas ultimate reserves given in Fig. 2 are higher than have been given in the past, where gas was estimated to be one half oil, but the equality figure does represent some modern thought.

WORLD DEMAND FOR OIL

Industrialised countries
During the past 25 years oil has been taking the place of coal as one of the primary sources of heating, in addition to the use of petroleum products to

fuel prime-movers and to make electrical power. In this period there has been a doubling of demand for petroleum products every 10 years, corresponding to an annual increase of 7–8%. It is interesting to consider how this increase has occurred. The developed countries such as the USA call for an extra 4% of petroleum every year. This is due partly to the few per cent increase in population, but also to the increase of individual wealth in the United States. More families have two or three automobiles instead of one; the young are earning and spending more money than ever before. The latter phenomenon is a result of industrialisation, where mass-production can be serviced by quickly trained people, as opposed to the long apprenticeship that was necessary in the previous age of hand-made goods. More spending money not only means that more manufactured apparatus is required, but also more electric power to operate the heaters, cooling units, TV sets, display signs etc. that are a part of the modern way of life.

Underdeveloped countries

At the opposite end of the gross-national-product scale are agricultural countries such as India, where the demand for petroleum rises slowly at about 2–4% per annum. In such developing countries there are few motor cars, and few machines to help the human hands make more of the luxuries of life. However, it is often the least-developed countries that have the high birth rates and are increasing the problem of world energy supply. The modern media of communication are efficient enough to pass the message to poor people that a happier life can be had if advantage is taken of industrialisation and if cheap mass-produced mechanical aids and tools are made available. Whether such countries as India will ever be able to change from an agricultural life, in view of their rapid increase in numbers, remains to be seen. Judging by remarks of the Indian leaders, it is possible that they may opt for continuing with a largely agricultural labour-intensive economy, and thereby live a more pleasant life, suited to the warm climate of India, rather than enter the industrial rat-race led by the developed countries.

Rapidly developing countries

If it is not the fully industrialised countries or the under-developed nations who create the large demand for oil products, who then accounts for the 7–8% annual increase which has continued since 1946? It is, of course, the 'take-off' countries such as Japan, Mexico and Spain who, in the course of a few years, alter their way of life from a poor, agricultural system to booming American-style industrialisation. The growth period of 10–20 years calls for a great injection of power and, since the prime energy source of the present period is petroleum, the sales of oil products to these countries rises at the rate of 10–20%. This excessively high demand for oil has kept the average growth rate up to 7–8% per year.

The world contains many nations, and it is probable that the demand for oil, or at least for energy, will continue at present rates for some time; this is because, when countries such as Japan ease off their rapid rate of increasing oil consumption, other energetic peoples will enter the take-off era from agricultural to industrial life. However, some new factors may alter the rate of increase during the next few decades. For a start, people have become increasingly aware of the problems of pollution. These are bound up very much with the increase of both population and industry. With small cities, sewage could safely be disposed of in seas and rivers, but in a population explosion the water becomes overladen with filth. Figure 3 shows the annual oil consumption per head in selected areas of the world at an interval of ten years, demonstrating the different demand patterns for different countries.

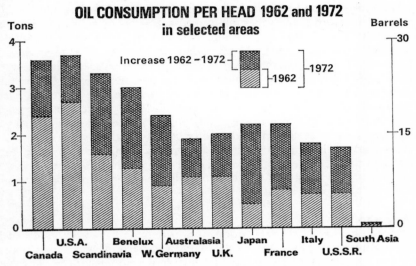

FIG. 3. Oil consumption per head 1962 and 1972 in selected areas.

The world oil consumption in 1972 was 2600 million tons. If the increase during the past 25 years continues, the amount for 1980 would be over 4000 million tons, and a doubling every decade would give 64 000 million tons by 2020. At this rate the 300 000 million tons would rapidly be used. However, oil demand will probably taper off around the end of this century because of the cut-down due to conservationist thinking and the advent of nuclear energy to take over a part of the oil-heating load. By 1990 the demand could be only 5000–6000 million tons, with 7000–8000 million tons as the figure for the year 2000. This could well be the top of the demand peak and could be maintained well beyond 2050.

RECOVERY RATES

Normal production

Since oil is contained in minute pores in the rock reservoir, only a fraction of the oil flows to producing wells. The percentage production varies enormously from one field to another, as might be expected on account of the large range of pore size distribution and permeability of reservoir rocks. The rates of recovery on normal flow may be as low as 15 % of oil in place, and as high as 50 %. With new fields, estimates of recovery are made based on measurements of rock properties of core samples, and on the physical characteristics of the reservoir crude oil. When a considerable amount of oil has been produced from a new field changes in pressure and of gas/oil and oil/water levels make it possible to revise original estimates based on core analysis.

In general the world reserve figures for non-proven oil take into consideration the probability of using the best production techniques. These may include gas injection to maintain reservoir pressure and thus avoid expensive pumping operations, and water injection which usually produces a great deal more oil than plain flow production. It is probable that water flooding in Kirkuk in Iraq, for example, has more than doubled the ultimate production of oil, while in Saudi Arabia 80% displacement efficiency is claimed for water injection. In many cases the extra oil produced by water flood is cheaper than that originally obtained by natural production, since a few injection wells are capable of supplying all the water needed. With gas fields a competent water drive may lead to a lower ultimate recovery because large blocks of formation may be sealed off by the water by-passing through fissures.

Gas injection is more expensive than water-flooding, but may give good results in fields where production depends on gravity drainage, owing to lowering of the viscosity of the reservoir fluid and to expansion of the crude oil due to absorption of gas.

Tertiary recovery
The nomenclature of oil-field production has grown somewhat confused in that secondary recovery, that is gas or water injection, which was once a new idea, is now taken for granted in oil field development. The petroleum engineers decide the best course of treatment for a field, and this may include some form of injection, either right from the start of production or at a later date. Other methods of squeezing further oil from the rock have been tried both in the laboratory and in pilot plants in oil fields, but the experiments outside the laboratory have been only very marginally successful.

One hopeful technique was to burn part of the oil *in situ* in order to warm the remainder so that the viscosity of the oil would be lowered. Injection of steam was another method designed to achieve a similar effect. Injection of LPG, or of 'miscible fluids' showed great promise in the laboratory, when all the oil in tubes packed with sand could be readily flushed out. The snag of all these methods is that in nature rock layers are seldom uniform either sideways or vertically and changes occur in permeability and porosity, together with shale breaks and other facies changes. This causes by-passing of injected gases, which often get lost rather than moving with displaced oil to the production wells, and also dying out of fires in underground burning.

In general, the new 'tertiary' methods of recovery will be expensive, and perhaps should be classified with treatment of tar sands and shales, in that they are at present not economically sound, but that they could be applied in places where the location of oil is known and therefore do not carry further exploration costs. The water and gas injection gains are today counted as normal good production practice and their effect on ultimate reserves has been taken into account in most of the estimates that have been presented recently.

NEW SOURCES OF OIL

Modern exploration

The question arises, where is the remainder of the ultimate world holding of 300 000 million tons to be found? It is not within the scope of this paper to give details of prospects in all areas of the world, even if these were known with any certainty, but it is useful to indicate where the oil could come from. During the past twenty years many parts of the world such as Alaska and Libya have been shown to contain large reserves of oil. These were not traditional oil bearing areas in the pre-war days, and the lesson to be learned from the past 25 years of oil discovery is that oil is much more widespread in its occurrence than had been supposed. There is a very good reason for this. The early oil discoveries were of shallow reservoirs, which almost invariably gave a clue to their presence by being associated with seepages of oil or gas to the surface. Now that geophysical techniques and drilling ability make it economically possible to find and drill structures at depths of more than 10 000 ft, a new exploration philosophy has grown up. These deep reservoirs, and particularly those offshore, do not reveal themselves by surface seepages. However, experience has shown that thick sedimentary basins often contain oil reservoirs, and therefore it must be assumed that all such geological features are worth some exploration effort. Geological reasoning with the help of magnetic surveys can make an assessment of the thickness of sediments. The area of a basin must be of a certain size to form a hopeful prospect, but the oil bearing northern part of the North Sea shows that such basins may be only hundreds of miles in extent, so that there are very many unexplored territories which are waiting to be prospected.

The recent discoveries in northern USSR suggest that an enormous potential exists along the Arctic regions, and with the support provided by discoveries in Alaska, the whole of the land areas facing towards the North Pole are places where oil of the future may be found. Although not much success has rewarded previous efforts in South America south of Venezuela, the large sedimentary basins may well contain large reservoirs. Now that oil fields at depths greater than 10 000 ft can be both located and exploited economically the whole sedimentary volume available to the oil finder is much enlarged, and therefore a reappraisal should be made in many places where, in the past, inadequate seismic techniques and drilling have suggested that no oil exists.

Unfortunately, as was pointed out earlier, oil fields are small dots in a sedimentary basin, giving a chance of less than one in a thousand of finding an economic reservoir at random. Good geology and geophysics reduce the odds to about one in ten (a statistical figure based on wildcat drilling over the past 10 years), so that in order to find the new oil that is needed for the next 50 years, encouragement must be given to drilling many exploratory bore-holes in order to beat the odds.

Small oil fields

A considerable amount of oil produced in the USA has come from small fields, where wells produce tens or hundreds of barrels a day, rather than the thousands of barrels a day of the Middle East or the North Sea. It is probable that these small fields would not be economic if all the discovery costs were included, but in the USA the depletion allowance must have had a beneficial effect. It is possible also that to some extent oil field gambling takes the place of football pools in the US and that a considerable amount of risk money is lost while the one in ten discovery is made.

These small oil fields may well be worth while in the future when the price of oil increases, and their output could supply a substantial part of the ultimate world reserves. Looking ahead to the time when a greater percentage of crude oil is used for chemicals or protein, small fields could well be the centre of chemical complexes, since the quantity of oil required is much less than that taken by refineries for conversion into fuels.

Offshore oil

As mentioned earlier, the continental shelves of the world hold large reserves of oil. Offshore exploration is the rapidly developing activity of the industry at the present time. This activity follows the trend of other oil production in that it is more expensive than previous land operations. However, because seismic reflection methods are about a hundred times quicker at sea than on land it is both slightly cheaper and much more speedy to collect results at sea than on land. Therefore the continental shelf areas of the world are receiving a great deal of attention, and discoveries that have been made offshore in places such as Australia and the North Sea are examples of what is to come.

Production offshore is expensive, since drilling costs are many times those on land, and development costs for original types of drilling and production platforms are large. It is fortunate that the industry has graduated from shallow water in the Gulf of Mexico through more difficult conditions in the Persian Gulf to the really arduous climate environment of the North Sea.

The North Sea has provided large gas fields, and oil production which could equal that of Kuwait during the past ten years. This is a fine example of the new look in exploration, which should realise that any sedimentary area is worth examination. There are more sea areas around the United Kingdom, and although they are for the most part in deeper water than the 450 ft of the BP Forties Field, the techniques of exploration and production are keeping pace with the more stringent requirements associated with deeper water, more severe weather conditions and oil reservoirs at greater depth than in the past.

The new engineering skills associated with offshore production appear to be well able to look after immediate problems of water depths of around 500 ft, and many good studies are being made in preparation for extending production to more than 1000 ft depth of water. It has been suggested that there may be large oil accumulations on the continental slopes, where the land geological formations join the deep ocean regime. The water depths here will increase from 1000 to 18 000 ft, and new engineering will be needed to solve production problems. The discovery technique of the geophysical seismic method is probably adequate for these deeper water regions. Seismic reflection has improved beyond measure during the past 5–10 years owing to the use of the computer and advanced techniques of stacking and cross-correlation. It would have been impossible to locate many of the North Sea structures ten years ago. The ability to drill in the deepest parts of the ocean has been demonstrated over the past three years by the Glomar Challenger, from which ship bore-holes have been drilled through many parts of the sediments of the deep sea floor in all the oceans. The sediments, as had been expected from earlier seismic measurements, are thin, and it is unlikely that accumulations of oil have occurred; there has not been as much concentration of animal life in the deep oceans as in shallow continental shelf seas and there do not appear to be many of the gently folded structures which are needed to house large oil reservoirs. If oil were to be found in the 18 000 ft depths of the oceans the engineering problems would be difficult but not insurmountable, but the expense of production would be very great.

THE FUTURE

Although the fossil fuel oil is only a temporary phase in the energy picture for human beings, there is no need for panic in that a gentle phasing out of oil demand can take place over the next 40 years or so, when nuclear energy (and possibly later on solar energy) takes the place of oil as a fuel. This phasing out entails an increase in production until the end of the century, followed by a steady period of production and refining. The recent interest in world energy should be very salutary to the human race in that it will cause an increase in price of oil and hence of energy of all sorts; this in turn will bring forward more expensive forms of oil to fill the energy gap temporarily. The after-effect of an increase in price will be a better appreciation of the value of energy in this world, so that heat is conserved by better insulation and by more efficient combustion. The age of profligate use of energy, led by the US, is coming to an end and energy from all sources must be appreciated at its real value.

REFERENCES

1. *BP Statistical Review of World Oil Industry* (1972).
2. H. R. Warman (1972). 'The future of oil', *Geographical J.*, **138**(3), 287–92.
3. L. G. Weeks (1971). 'Marine geology and petroleum resources', *in Proceedings of the 8th World Petroleum Congress, Moscow*, Vol. 2, pp. 99–106, Applied Science, London.

Discussion

Mr J. M. C. Bishop (Phillips Petroleum Co. Ltd): Dr Gaskell stated that as market prices increase, companies will be able to get into more expensive production areas and develop more expensive technologies. How do you see these developments being financed when the revenue arising from the increased prices goes to governments and not to the companies that have to make the investments?

Dr Gaskell: I don't know too much about the political side but I think it is up to the oil industry to make sure it does get an adequate return for the money it invests. Governments have learned by example that there are various rules that apply to oil industries. The most successful country in the business of small oilfields is the United States. Small oilfields are encouraged there by various forms of price control, of depletion allowances and so on; and if the human beings of this world want more oil, governments have got to encourage oil companies to find it. The North Sea Gas price at wellhead is far too low and was based on advice from the United States Federal Gas people who have ruined their own gas exploration industry by setting far too low prices, based to some extent on the value of associated gas rather than gas found by itself. We have now found that exploration for gas alone in the North Sea is falling off because the price wasn't pitched right. So I think the political answer to a political question is that it is up to governments to encourage oil companies by allowing satisfactory financial return.

Mr K. A. D. Inglis (British Petroleum Co. Ltd): I'd like to reinforce both what the last contributor and Dr Gaskell said. There is not only the considerable problem of convincing the government of the absolute necessity for adequate returns—not only in the oil industry, but in the entire energy industry. There is also a very considerable problem in the attitude of the consumer which, in a sense, we in the oil industry have been responsible for creating for ourselves.

Here a willingness to face up to the long-term prospects of higher cost energy is moving very slowly indeed. I delayed my arrival at Harrogate to attend what was effectively a public protest meeting at Canvey Island on the construction of refineries there. The people in that meeting represented consumer interests, local authorities and national government.

The general attitude on the part of everybody who participated except the two people from the oil industry, was that not only was the Middle East such a prolific source of oil that it could go on for donkey's years anyway, but that the oil companies were labelled as a big source of money. In fact they could be expected to carry all the uneconomic indulgencies, such as building refinery capacity for the South East of England up in the far north of Scotland without the customer having to pay any penalty whatsoever.

So it's not only a matter of persuading governments who, although they may claim to realise this point, in their actions very frequently deny it, but also in getting over these fundamental facts to the public in general.

I would like to ask Mr Broadbent about the very considerable research and development effort that is called for in the coal industry.

The coal industry suffered during the 'twenties and 'thirties from exactly the same problems as the oil industry over the last twelve years—from incredibly low rates of return. In absolute terms in the UK the rate of return on coal was between 3d and 6d a ton throughout that period despite the value of money going down very sizeably. The need not only for research and development, but also for investment, was growing all the time.

Mr Broadbent mentioned that there is a R and D effort called for from the coal industry of a very considerable size, perhaps comparable in terms of potential expenditure with that which has gone into nuclear energy during the last 25 years. I would like to hear Mr Broadbent's comments on where the money is going to come from in order to mount this sort of effort.

Mr Broadbent: It really is a matter of the education of people and hence government. People who want a standard of living are going to have to pay for it, either for the commodity itself or in the form of taxation. I believe the cost of things and the price of things are two functions which do, generally speaking, move together. They go in stepped functions and they don't always step together so that sometimes you even get a cross-over.

In the short term they may reverse, and I think the oil industry at this moment is going through the same problems we have been through in coal. However, if you take the long-term (20, 30, 40 years) graph of this, the two lines will go up more or less together.

In the case of the NCB, we are a nationalised industry, therefore there is no problem when it comes to who pays. It is our shareholders—that is the government. In the oil industry it might be a form of taxation release or incentive of this nature. In all cases the customer pays.

Mr N. White (Hambros Bank): Is it a fair generalisation to say that the so-called US energy crisis would not have existed had there not been an environmental lobby? For instance, more nuclear power stations would have been built had it not been for this lobby. Similarly, there would have been more coal in the United States if it had not been for the environmental lobby against strip mining.

First, are most of the world's coal reserves at a depth where cheap strip mining is likely to be practical? Secondly, does he see a major environmental problem being caused if coal is to fill the so-called gap in the energy supply?

Mr Broadbent: Although the environmental lobby has accelerated the identification of the energy gap theory, by short term restrictions on the operations of new nuclear stations or of strip mining activities, I don't think that the environment alone is the real root of the problem.

The real problem is that fossil fuels are like a deposit account. Once you have spent the deposit you have got no money in the bank. If it is there, how you get it out and whether it can satisfy everyone environmentally is simply a matter of cost. Until adequate nuclear or solar energy is available, fossil fuels will be needed to maintain our standard of living and rate of growth. As we go from an era of low fuel costs to an era of high fuel costs, individuals will make their decision as to whether they have a holiday abroad, or have a warm house in London.

On the question of the reserves, I do not know the exact breakdown between that which could be deep mined and strip mined, but there is no doubt that the strip mining of vast amounts of coal and of the other things like tar sands and shale is possible. Both in England and America we see a lot of development of the strip mining process. What is more, the new machines can go down deeper as strip mining techniques improve, this means that what years ago would have been a deep mine can now almost be a strip mine.

There is also a great push ahead on drift mines which go in at an angle down to the coal and save winding problems since you can use conveyor belts.

We design a mine now not just as a shaft but as a much more unified system where the cutting rate equals the conveying rate which equals the washing and preparation rate.

Mr G. F. Skelton (Consultant): History has shown that we (the world) have doubled the rate of offtake of crude oil in the last ten years.

How soon would it be physically possible to double the rate of production of coal using modern technology and available manpower?

Mr Broadbent: The Americans intend to double their coal production in ten years. In the UK, our rundown of numbers of men has been over half to about 300 000 now, against 600 000–700 000 ten years or so ago.

The hope is that with fully integrated mining systems from mechanisation, the output could stay the same or go up. We are planning to stabilise at the present 140–150 million tons a year. Up till now production has been going down. We are now stabilising and then, of course, we look to the future and a rise in production. What it will eventually go up to depends on a number of things.

Mr G. F. Skelton: If we are looking at this resource to take the place of oil, we have to look at it increasing.

Mr Broadbent: On present day knowledge I agree with you. But I think we have now got to look ahead to the better, more efficient use of the fuel, and husbanding of resources. Although I draw coal production in a curve that goes up by 1·83%—not an ambitious curve—even so I think that has got to be reduced.

Mr J. D. Davis (Shell Composites): Previous speakers referred to the need for governments and the general population to accept that oil company operations must be profitable if finance for growth is to be available. Let us not forget that over many years industry policies have been pursued which have resulted in most profit being generated in production with little if any from downstream operations. Against this background it is going to be very difficult to convince people that what has apparently worked for many years is no longer feasible—particularly if downstream operations continue to operate on a false commercial basis. To a considerable extent this problem is one that the industry has created for itself.

I was astonished to hear Mr Broadbent say that in recent years in the UK there has been no net increase in coal industry investment—depreciation has matched new investment. If coal is to provide an increasing contribution to the UK energy picture, what assurance can we have, in face of past performance, that the very large capital sums of money will be generated or otherwise raised. This surely is likely to be a major bottleneck unless there is a fundamental change.

Another potentially serious bottleneck is the provision of high quality manpower—by no means all traditional miners—who will be required to work underground. Despite increased mechanisation deep mining will surely be relatively manpower intensive. What are the prospects of obtaining a satisfactory workforce in the long-term?

Mr Broadbent: What guarantee have we got that this investment increase will produce an increase in tonnage of coal? I must say that we are not looking at this moment in time for an increase in UK coal output, but we must consider world coal.

The only guarantee we have got is the need for it. The amount of investment will, therefore, have to make this possible. You have to invest in new machinery to get this strip mining working, you have to invest in new techniques to make strip mining acceptable to the public who also want the energy. And they will have to come to their decision as to whether they want more environmental control put into this and hence pay more, and investment will be greater. It is all the stepped function which I have been talking about. The government in this country have shown their faith in the ability of the mining industry by giving us recent recognition in the form of independent corporate status, and there is no doubt that they are looking upon coal as their insurance policy for future energy.

Obviously our aim must be to get high productivity from the manpower we have got, and we expect to produce the same tonnage of coal with even less manpower. We are also very conscious that ultimately, one of the ecological problems will be the difficulty of sending men down a hole in the ground. It is ultimately going to be anti-social to do this sort of thing. The only encouraging thing at this moment of time is that the person who worries least about it is the active miner. We are actually recruiting younger men.

I do not think we will have any difficulty getting the number needed at the time with the correct productivity rate. I think that Professor Thring has got some very good ideas on the automation; in fact in the Daily Telegraph today there was mention of some automatic device.

All these will play a part and now we are getting by-products from the space age and more sophisticated equipment items. There is no doubt that the idea of an automat going down and doing something is rather splendid, but I think it is the man with the hammer who goes down and hits the right place who gets the thing working.

Professor P. R. Odell (Erasmus University, Rotterdam):

1. Consumers, governments etc. still need to have the case for energy shortage and traumatically increased prices of energy *proven* rather than stated. (Compare the traditional arguments in these respects with the evaluated profitability on North Sea oil production, delivered to an on-shore terminal, at $3/brl.) If oil prices rise above this then North Sea oil becomes 'too profitable' to eliminate the greater attentions of governments at least; this also has the effect of attracting new investment in the industry, so increasing supply and perhaps, even in the relatively short term future, converting 'scarcity' into yet another surplus!

2. Both speakers tended to concentrate on the long-term future rather than the next 12 years—as required by the subject of this session! Perhaps this means for this period that both speakers accept a continuation of the 'status quo': *viz.* the continuing decline in coal and doubling of oil production?

3. Why does Dr Gaskell accept the idea that ultimate oil reserves have settled down at $\simeq 2000 \times 10^9$ brls? Statistical analysis of the trend over the last 30 years shows an almost perfectly fitting straight line development of ideas about ultimate reserves (*see* my Fig. 1)—with no recent downturn in the area. Why should this not continue given increasing knowledge about oil and its occurrence?

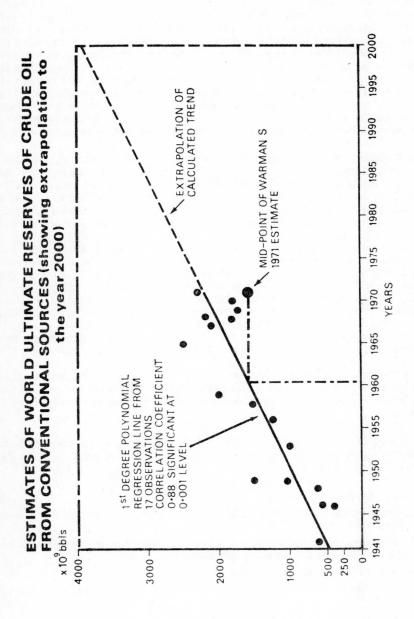

ESTIMATES OF WORLD ULTIMATE RESERVES OF CRUDE OIL FROM CONVENTIONAL SOURCES (showing extrapolation to the year 2000)

Dr Gaskell: All these figures are estimates. The very fact that the latest figures are not greater than some of the ones suggested by Weeks several years ago does suggest that there are good reasons to believe this may be the ultimate limit. We have looked in the last ten years at many new sedimentary areas. We are getting a much better idea of the geology in parts of the world we have not looked at closely before. On the other hand, I have heard, over 25 years in the oil company, true stories of geologists who have threatened to drink all the oil they may find in places like Bahrain and Saudi Arabia. I think I have taken into account the possibility of a straight line increase. My advice to people who look for oil at 5000 ft in their country is to go back and have a look with better geophysics and deeper drilling. Even so I know there must be a limit to the amount of oil in a place and I think those figures could be the most likely since they are a concensus of various carefully studied appraisals.

Mr Broadbent: In the short term in this country, we are looking for stabilisation of coal production at its present level, while the USA plans to increase its production by 50% in the next 10 years. World-wide the idea is to increase coal production. In this country we are consolidating a lot of our coal mines. Where a field may be punctured by three shafts, we are trying to consolidate it into one wide shaft; that will make for more efficiency and then if the expansion is possible it will be easier to expand on those faces.

There are not many new processes or new ideas that come to fruition in less than 10 years. It is probably nearer 15 years by the time we have got the techniques right, have obtained planning permission and built and commissioned. Some of these ideas are still at the laboratory stage. One thing that will help production is strip mining. It has very low manpower needs and is done for us by contractors.

We have made great strides in rehabilitating the land after strip mining activities, producing for the local people the sort of hills or dales or fields they want. To some extent we have overcome this terrible thing of the past, that once you have strip mined you have ruined the place. We are now beginning to advise people in America on how to do it successfully.

We have the expertise in this country and know where a lot of coal is available for strip mining when we need it. But at the moment this is a reserve or margin we must keep in case OPEC or American investment in oil now were to pinch us very severely.

Dr Gaskell: I have not mentioned anything about the short term: what I said was 'demand would double between 1970 and 1980, by present methods', but after that perhaps things will ease up.

Mr C. L. Goodacre (Consultant):

1. Does so called 'clean' 'low-sulphur' coal have a lower Btu content than normal 'high-sulphur' coal?
2. Therefore for a given energy production does more 'low-sulphur' coal have to be used creating an increasing ash disposal problem?
3. Is 'low-sulphur' coal in short supply?
4. What percentage of world's coal availability is so called 'clean low-sulphur coal'?

Mr Broadbent: It is difficult to generalise about coal. You get some low-sulphur with a high Btu value and vice-versa. A major need for the low-sulphur coals is for use in coke-making for the steel industry. A low sulphur content is probably more important for steel making than to avoid air pollution.

Mr C. L. Goodacre: There are two discrepancies in Mr Broadbent's paper. He talks about greater efficiency in energy use. Earlier he described the Coal Board's research activities in developing liquefaction and gasification methods for solid fuel. Although undoubtedly in themselves these processes may be viable there seems to be a contradiction of what was said later on about improving efficiency in the use of energy. Perhaps some technique of burning coal can be developed which can cope with the ash problem that current methods of coal produce. By converting solid fuel to gas you not only use up energy, but it also costs money.

Mr Broadbent: Yes, the point is that the major unit in the Coalplex would be the power station, producing electricity. Really what we are trying to do is use the energy in the coal more efficiently, and not only that which can be obtained by straight electricity generation.

Miss M. P. Doyle (Esso Petroleum Co. Ltd): Commenting on Professor Odell's implication that oil at $3/brl was a high price, current prices being paid for 'participation oil' and US experience in trying to obtain additional crude last winter, suggest $3/brl was in the past—not the future.

Has Mr Bagge from the US said where capital would come from to provide for the doubling of the US coal industry over the next 10 years? Secondly, what might be expected in terms of per cent increase in world oil reserves from the use of tertiary recovery methods?

Mr Broadbent: Well, Mr Bagge did not say where the capital was coming from, but I am seeing him next week and I will ask him.

Dr Gaskell: The figure for ultimate world reserves, estimated at about 300 000 million tons, includes what is more or less routine now—the use of gas and water injection, which used to be considered secondary recovery. I suppose in principle one could get a possible 30 or 40% increase to world reserves by tertiary methods such as underground burning. But I think tertiary recovery schemes are not going to be 100% efficient and they are going to be expensive.

The trouble is rock layers are not laid down in the nice neat fashion that you find in geological text books. While you can take a tube of sand filled with oil and flush 99% of it out in the laboratory, it does not work that way in practice, so tertiary recovery schemes could perhaps give a 20 or 30% increase but will not alter possible reserves by any great order of magnitude. They are not going to suddenly alter the whole energy picture.

Mr G. Lees (Shell-Mex and B.P.): The conciliatory attitudes of both coal and oil interests are most gratifying. However, both speakers confined their expressions to the 'up-stream' function. In terms of the 'down-stream' end one is interested in the level of agreement on the division of end use. Would the coal interests, for instance, be prepared to accept say 90% of their production being devoted to electricity generation and leave the exploitation of the general industrial trade sector to oil?

The problem of manpower would seem to be a major obstacle to the expansion of coal. Whilst the level of productivity has doubled in the past decade, this has been largely due to mechanisation. With this transition now largely accomplished, a situation of diminishing returns must now apply and one is led to ask how a further substantial increase in productivity is to be achieved.

Mr Broadbent: On the utilisation point, I think you can reduce the demand considerably by one thing in this country—house insulation. By simple house insulation becoming economically viable, you could reduce the growth of demand by a considerable amount. The Coal Board has joint research programmes with oil companies in this country and America on the future utilisation of coal. We want to extend this co-operation with all energy producing interests. On your first question, I believe strongly that you should never burn gas if you can burn oil, and you should never burn oil if you can burn coal. In other words the cheapest way of getting oil from coal is to burn coal by substitution, and thus leave gas and oil for better purposes.

On the manpower question, the sort of thing that we are doing includes a nuclear sensing device which follows the seam of coal which can be very irregular. This device uses the coal seam to steer the cutting machine, which reduces the number of men who would otherwise be required. More accurate and speedy conveyance of coal is eliminating the need for belt men to pick up the lumps that fall off. The pumps are being designed from different materials, to ensure continuity of operations, so we do not need to send a man down to maintain it. Plug-in type electronics is now being worked on, so that we do not send a man down to do maintenance below ground, instead you put in a replacement module. All this is aimed at reducing manpower down on the face.

· CHAPTER 4

Natural Gas—Growth of a World Market

P. F. CORBETT

British Petroleum Co. Ltd, London, UK
(Presented by J. G. Stainer, British Petroleum Co. Ltd)

GLOBAL VIEW

To review the subject of natural gas on a world-wide basis is to produce a series of sketches on different aspects and of different areas only very lightly held together by a common theme. To the extent that (a) natural gas is located, assessed, produced and transported by techniques and with equipment used for similar activities with oil, and (b) a high proportion of the natural gas available is produced (or could be produced) in association with the production of liquid petroleum products, natural gas is part of the oil industry. Its marketing might therefore be thought to have paralleled that of oil.

However, its international market penetration has been uneven and only in a few countries (or even in specific regions of a single country) has the market for gas been developed commensurate with available reserves. Until very recently it has been necessary to establish an adequate and secure distribution system for transporting the gas to areas of high energy demand within the country in which the gas source is located. In the USA, Canada and the USSR where, in each case, a single political control exists over the long-distance pipeline system, indigenous natural gas has for some time made a major contribution to primary energy supplies. Other important sources of gas, however, are separated either politically and/or geographically from potential markets and it has required a large measure of co-operation between states, gas producers and potential consumers to overcome some of the resultant difficulties.

In the last few years, however, we have seen such co-operation resulting in (a) the construction, in both Europe and Asia, of overland pipelines and intermediate compression stations permitting gas to be delivered over international frontiers, and (b) the completion of integrated schemes for liquefying gas and storing it at or near the gas source, its transport in specially constructed and insulated ocean-going tankers and its reception, storage, regasification (and subsequent distribution in gaseous form) in the country of its potential market. We believe that these types of joint venture will continue to be

45

developed and that the natural gas industry will become more flexible in its international marketing arrangements.

In 1968 the present author and T. F. Gaskell[1] suggested that the newly discovered natural gas sources in North Western Europe were likely to be developed and supply 10% of the total energy demands of Western Europe by the mid 1970s. It is clear from the 'actual' figures recorded in Table 1 that

TABLE 1

Actual (1971) and Projected (1980) Consumption of Natural Gas by Areas

Area	Million metric tons oil equivalent				% natural gas of total energy (nearest %)	
	Natural gas		Total energy			
	1971	1980	1971	1980	1971	1980
Western Europe	87	225	1 055	1 700	8	13
Eastern Europe	30	65	316	460	10	14
Japan	3	40	287	650	1	6
Australasia	2	15	57	100	4	15
Near and Middle East, India and rest of Far East, excluding China	16·5	65	230	500	7	13
Africa	3	5	102	170	3	3
USA	550	690	1 592	2 300	35	30
Canada	38·5	75	149	250	26	30
Central and South America	31	55	209	400	15	14
USSR	164	520	900	1 600	18	32
China	3	5	300	450	1	1
World	928	1 760	5 197	8 580	18	21
World (excluding USA)	378	1 070	3 605	6 280	10	17

this estimate is certain to be confirmed in practice. From the experiences in Europe and elsewhere over the last five years, and using additional sources of information, some further estimates are presented on a world-wide basis to cover the next decade. These and current data for other regions of the world are also shown in the same table from which some broad conclusions can be drawn.

The use of natural gas will continue to expand, certainly over the next decade, with developments, in percentage increase terms, greatest in selected areas outside the US. Over this short period the world consumption of natural gas is expected to double and its share of the total energy market on a global basis to increase from 18 to 21%. In the US, in spite of the consumption of an extra 140 million tons of fuel oil equivalent, natural gas is not expected to maintain its current market share in 1980. Excluding consumption in the US, the natural gas market in the rest of the world is believed to be capable of almost trebling its market in the next decade. The rise of the natural gas industry outside the US is even more dramatically illustrated if one includes also a decade in retrospect. By 1980 natural gas consumption world-wide should have increased by a factor of approximately four as compared with 1960: if data for the world excluding the US are considered over the same period the factor is almost 12. Areas already contributing to this development and expected further to increase their consumption of natural gas are Western and Eastern Europe, Japan, Australasia and the USSR.

In Chapter 3, Gaskell quoting Warman[2] has put the world sources of natural gas as equivalent to those of oil, but not all are so close to high energy consuming areas as to be easily exploitable. The production and consumption of natural gas from North and West Africa and the Middle and Far East in particular, involve a wide range of technical, economic, physical and political considerations which, as far as is possible, have been taken into account in the projections presented above.

UNITED STATES

Any review of natural gas markets must start with the US. Although natural gas has always been available in isolation and in small amounts arising from the degradation of vegetable and animal material, its availability in bulk dates from the earliest days of the oil industry when it appeared as a somewhat embarrassing by-product of liquid petroleum production. In these early years, when the markets for petroleum products were mainly for kerosine and motor spirit, the lighter gaseous and the heavier residual factions were not so easy to market. The market for gas was particularly difficult to establish as its low thermal density presented both physical and economic problems of storage and transport as compared with the liquid fuels which become available from the heavier end of the barrel.

Applications where (at that time) a gaseous fuel had advantage (*e.g.* domestic cooking and lighting, and street lighting) could be supplied cheaply by gas manufactured from coal in plants close to the urban demand area; natural gas on the other hand was not always so near at hand. In the US some 90% of the total gas reserves are in the States of Texas, Louisiana, Oklahoma, Kansas and New Mexico (and offshore Gulf of Mexico), whereas the most important of the energy markets are in the more populated and industrialised and colder areas of the north-eastern States (and to a lesser extent in other areas). Even though natural gas was indigenous, the US gas market only expanded with the development of long distance pipeline transmission systems into these areas. Tables 2 and 3 illustrate the correlation between gas sales, pipeline construction and inter-State movement of gas and the consequential penetration of gas into the energy markets.

Of some significance too are the differences between the gas markets in the producing States and those in the non-producing ones. In the producing States about 90% of the gas used is for electricity generation, oil producers' field requirements or in industry generally; in the north-eastern States sales into the domestic sector are about 70% of the total market. It is the revenues from the higher tariffed domestic and commercial markets which make the long distance movement of gas an economic proposition.

But an increasing commitment to the domestic market brings also its responsibilities. These must be (a) to meet peak demands in times of severe weather (b) to match the hourly changing rhythm of normal suburban life

TABLE 2

Development of Gas Sales (US) with Development of Inter-State Transmission System

Year	Total gas sales 10^{12} cu ft	High pressure transmission lines '000 miles	% gas sold outside producing states
1945	3·92	77	48
1950	6·28	109	52
1955	9·41	142	55
1960	12·77	181	60
1965	16·58	210	64
1970	21·90	253	67

TABLE 3

US Per Head Consumption of Energy and of Natural Gas, 1920–70

Year	Millions Btu		% natural gas of total
	Natural gas	Total energy	
1920	8	186	4
1930	16	181	9
1940	21	181	12
1950	41	226	18
1960	71	249	28
1970	110	338	33

and (c) to continue to supply the increased demands made by each individual customer as his comfort and convenience standards match the growing affluence of his society. The rate of development of the gas market in the US has now out-stripped the rate at which new indigenous sources of gas are becoming available. The ratio of proved reserves to annual consumption, which in 1966 was 16 to 1 is now down to 11 to 1. Even though Alaskan sources should become available in the long term, assessments (by many different authorities) of potential demand against future production lead to a view that by 1980 there could be a supply deficiency of at least 50 mtfoe and that this could double by 1985. Although energetic attention will be paid to coal and oil gasification, gas companies will undoubtedly need to use some imported natural gas to meet their customers' demands and it is these pressures which will both develop and to some extent change the role of natural gas in the world energy markets.

CONTINENTAL EUROPE

In Europe, until the mid 1960s indigenous sources of gas were used in areas relatively near to the source of supply and made small but significant contributions to the energy resources of Austria, France, Germany and Italy. In total, however, natural gas contributed somewhat less than 2% of the total energy required in Western Europe in 1960. The discovery of the Slochteren gas field (where reserves were considered more than adequate for internal consumption in The Netherlands) promoted the conclusion of contracts for the export of some of the gas and the consequential building of a pipeline distribution system from The Netherlands to serve the already existing gas industries of Belgium, France and Germany. This system is currently being expanded into Southern Germany and Italy to meet additional gas contracts in these areas. By 1970 the use of natural gas had increased seven fold and its contribution to the European total energy requirements was approximately 7%.

However, towards the end of the 1960s it became apparent that although the already concluded gas export contracts from The Netherlands and the internal Dutch requirements could be met from the reserves, extensions to the contracts were unlikely. At plateau production, commitments from Slochteren and associated fields appeared to be as listed in Table 4.

TABLE 4
Disposal of Dutch Gas into NW Europe

Country	Natural gas (mtfoe)
Western Germany	18
Belgium	9
France	7·5
Italy	4·5
Total exports	39
Netherlands	30
Total	69

Searches for gas elsewhere in Continental Europe have not been too rewarding. Some minor finds have been registered on shore, but in each case only sufficient to supply a small local area or a particular plant (Germany) or to add a small increment to other neighbouring sources (France and The Netherlands). Offshore exploration in Dutch, German, Italian and French areas has produced only one small field of commercial potential and until recently the disposal of this gas was in doubt owing to differences in attitude between the Dutch and German governments, presumably arising from anxiety about future gas supplies.

As a result of the apparent shortage of Dutch gas and the lack of new indigenous sources (and also possibly to have a wider variety of suppliers), the countries concerned sought to import gas from other areas, in particular from the USSR and North Africa.

Gas from the USSR is already supplied into Eastern Europe and into Austria via Czechoslovakia. Developing from this movement of gas, via a pipeline system through Austria, it is expected that about 7–10 million tons of gas will go to Austria and Italy, south Germany and France. Two contracts have been signed for Russian gas to be moved to the Ruhr and other

areas of Western Germany. Although not affected by the earlier developments from Holland, Scandinavia has now entered the natural gas markets.
A pipeline from Russia is under construction into Finland and about a
million tons should soon be available in that country. There is speculation as
to whether Russian gas will penetrate *via* Finland into other Scandinavian
countries, Sweden being particularly anxious to secure supplies in the near
future.

From time to time proposals are made that natural gas *via* North Germany
could enter Denmark but the geographical difficulties of distribution so far
have made the proposals uneconomic. The situation could change, however,
dependent upon the economics of transporting gas found in Danish North
Sea waters.

The inability of the Scandinavian countries to develop a natural gas market
similar to that in the more densely populated areas of Western Europe is
particularly demonstrated by the fact that about 8 million tons of fuel oil
equivalent of natural gas from the Ekofisk field in Norwegian waters is to
find its place in the European gas markets by pipeline to North Germany and
thence to The Netherlands, Belgium and France.

The second major source of imports into Western Europe is from North
Africa in the form of LNG. The exports from Algeria to the UK and France
in 1964/5 were the earliest commercial contracts for gas in this form. A little
later, when Northern Europe was expanding its gas industries on pipeline gas
from The Netherlands, Spain and Italy were looking to Libya for supplies
which became available in 1970/71. Emphasis has now moved back to large
reserves in Algeria and contracts have been concluded for further supplies
to France and Spain. Of major significance is the quite recently announced
contract between France, Belgium and some south German gas companies
with Algeria for LNG to move into two Mediterranean ports and thence by
pipeline to major areas of gas consumption. It is as yet too early to describe
the routes in detail, as the arrangements would seem to point to consequential
exchange deals between companies for gas from Dutch, North African and
Russian sources based on an appraisal of the optimisation of distribution
services throughout the area. A high degree of co-operation and integration
between the many countries and gas companies involved will obviously be
necessary.

In total, gas from North Africa into Europe will amount to about 18–20
mtfoe by the early 1980s, and this could be increased if a pipeline route
across the Mediterranean became a practical proposition. At the moment
the lack of pipe-laying experience in the depth of water involved appears to
rule out any such possibility for at least 10 years.

The actual (1971) and probable (1980) contributions of natural gas to the
energy markets of selected areas of Europe are given in Table 5. Included in
the forecasts are the gas imports believed to be possible; at the moment
they may account for about 4% of the gas consumed in Western Europe, but
by the late 1970s this proportion could be 15%, increasing to 25% in the
following five years. With the assumptions used for the development of
contracts and forecasted arrangements, some 75% of the growth in the
West European gas industry from 1977/78 to 1982/83 could be provided by
imported gas.

TABLE 5
Actual (1971) and Projected (1980) Consumption of Natural Gas in Europe

| Country | Million metric ton oil equivalent | | | | % natural gas of total energy (nearest %) | |
| | Natural gas | | Total energy | | | |
	1971	1980	1971	1980	1971	1980
Western Germany	16·8	52	235	340	7	15
Netherlands	21·1	40	61	100	35	40
Belgium	5·1	10	46	70	11	14
France	10·7	23	152	255	7	9
Italy	10·1	23	119	235	8	10
United Kingdom	18·5	50	206	275	9	18
The rest	4·4	27	236	425	2	6
Total	86·7	225	1 055	1 700	9	13

UNITED KINGDOM

The development of the gas market in the UK both before and after the discovery of natural gas in the North Sea has been more than adequately documented. It is interesting however to recapitulate the penetration both of the gas industry and of natural gas into the energy market of the UK (Table 6). As can be seen, the conversion programme is well advanced although the figures would also suggest that substantial new industrial loads have been secured. Some of these, it is certain, will be only of short duration and others will be seasonal contracts which must be more and more interrupted as the full effect of a developing domestic heating load begins to be felt.

Gas from the major fields in the southern half of the British North Sea is fully committed to the British Gas Corporation. Discussions are also being held with a view to BGC purchasing gas produced in association with crude oil from the discoveries in the northern area. Of greater significance however is that BGC is currently negotiating for supplies from the large Frigg accumulation lying partly in British and partly in Norwegian waters. Although BGC will in all probability secure the gas from the British sector, the ultimate

TABLE 6
Per Cent Contribution to Energy Requirements

Year	1960	1964	1965	1966	1967	1968	1969	1970	1971
Manufactured gas	5·2	5·8	6·2	6·9	7·5	7·8	8·0	7·4	6·2
Natural gas (distributed to converted areas and plants)						0·2	0·7	2·5	6·5
Total	5·2	5·8	6·2	6·9	7·5	8·0	8·7	9·9	12·7

destination of the Norwegian sector gas is more problematical. These combined associated and non-associated sources are expected by 1980 to contribute 18% of total UK energy demand. Although still relying in the short term on indigenous supplies, medium-term requirements for energy may include the movement of gas into the UK from non-indigenous sources.

JAPAN

Japan has virtually no indigenous natural gas but is rapidly becoming an important natural gas consumer, relying on imports of LNG from Alaska and Brunei and (in the near future) from the Persian Gulf. The main attraction of natural gas to Japan is its clean burning characteristics. The high density of both population and industry and a rapid growth rate in fuel consumption over the last two decades has produced air pollution problems which the authorities believe can only be reduced by the use of low-sulphur fuel oil or sulphur-free natural gas.

The need for low-sulphur fuels has stimulated searches for natural gas in offshore waters, but in spite of two discoveries on the continental shelf it is not possible at this stage to assess the gas potential of the Sea of Japan. The urgency of the demand for natural gas however is such that schemes for the import of LNG have needed to be developed irrespective of the possibility of any potential indigenous gas production.

LNG was initially imported from Alaska in 1969 and is now being delivered at about 1·3 mtfoe. A second scheme involving gas from Brunei became operative in 1972 and when fully developed during the next four to five years is destined to deliver gas at about 6 mtfoe. The most recently agreed scheme is that for about 2 mtfoe from Abu Dhabi with initial deliveries scheduled for 1976. Schemes involving gas from Sarawak and Iran are also being actively promoted. Imports from both Russia and Australia are possibilities later in the decade, although the development of all new projects will be conditioned by the availability and price of alternative forms of energy such as low-sulphur fuel oils or nuclear power. The projections forward have included an assessment of the possible development of these schemes.

It is thought that only a small proportion of the total gas imports will go to domestic users. The bulk appears to be destined for thermal power stations—which have special responsibilities placed on them to control sulphur emission—and the balance to large industrial users faced with similar problems.

USSR

The extensive deposits of gas in USSR have already been partially developed for indigenous consumption and for export to Eastern Europe. Further increases in production are planned and the high pressure pipeline network is scheduled to be increased by 33% (to 160 000 miles) during the five year plan period 1971 to 1975. As well as increasing the length of the system the latest additions are of extra wide diameter, 48 inch being more or less standard and in many cases 56 inch diameter being provided. Steel pipe for these developments is included in the reasons for 'gas for pipelines' contracts with West Germany and now proposed to the US. The pipeline system is only partially required for exports, the majority being scheduled to provide a further 70 million of the population with a piped domestic gas supply.

Gas is imported from Iran to Baku in order to augment and later replace a declining indigenous gas production already connected to a developed pipeline system. At the moment these imports are greater than the exports to Europe but as the latter build up, the USSR will become a net gas exporter of some significance.

Russian sources will obviously provide gas for Eastern Europe and may further penetrate into Scandinavia. From published production plans and contracted export arrangements it would seem that by 1980 there will still be ample scope for further exports. However, the practicability of many schemes must be tested against the availability of capital, the capacity of steel mills and the degree to which technical knowledge and manpower can be found. However, these could be part of package barter deals involving further gas exports, and may not be so constraining as appear at first sight.

OTHER AREAS

In most other parts of the world gas is used to meet indigenous needs which tend to be small in relation to the requirements of the highly industrialised societies. Significant volumes of gas are, however, used locally in Mexico, Trinidad, Colombia, Venezuela, Pakistan, Afghanistan, New Zealand, Australia and Canada.

Canada has a large home market and also exports by pipeline to the USA. Little growth has taken place recently in these exports owing to the Canadians' wish to first establish sufficient reserves to meet domestic requirements for 25 years. However, prospects in the Canadian arctic are good and it is probable that within the next decade arctic gas will be moving by trans-Canadian pipeline to US markets.

In New Zealand the currently producing onshore Kapuni field supplies the small domestic markets of the gas industries of the North Island; while the recently discovered offshore Maui field is likely to supply the thermal power stations planned to cater for a rapidly growing market for electricity. It remains to be seen whether any gas will be liquefied for consumption on the South Island or for export.

In Australia fields on and offshore in the South and East of the continent are supplying gas to the States in those areas; recent discoveries in the North West Shelf could be more than sufficient for areas along the west and north coasts. Although the Government has announced plans for an integrated inter-State distribution system, the long distances and the thinly populated areas between a few main centres of energy consumption must make the economics suspect except on a long-term strategic basis. The possibility of exports to the West coast of the US or to Japan should not be discounted if it can be proved that there are adequate reserves to sustain all local requirements at least to the end of this century.

Outside the US the largest gas reserves are in the Middle East and North and West Africa. Although small local requirements for gas are met by current production from Nigeria and the Middle East states, any schemes further to develop gas production in these and in other areas must be based on an assumed export market. These have been seen to be confined to the US, Western Europe and Japan and although theoretically there should be free competition between these areas (and reasons for them in the cases of US and Europe), in fact the shipping distances between source and potential market will in the main, dictate pseudo 'franchise areas' governed by the economics of transport imposed by geography.

LIQUEFIED NATURAL GAS

There is universal acceptance that the most rapidly developing sections of the natural gas industry are those associated with LNG. Much has already been written on this subject and the most recent review by Peebles[3] indicates a level of LNG trade in the 1980s of between a low of about 100 mtfoe and a high of about 200 mtfoe. At any level, Peebles forecasts that about half of the total LNG will move to US coasts with the remainder divided more or less evenly between Western Europe and Japan. Of special interest is his view of the possible 1980 price levels for the three areas which are placed (in USc/million Btu) at 80 to 120 for US East Coast, 100 to 150 for US West Coast, 75 to 100 for Europe and 80 to 150 for Japan. A shipping requirement of about 70–80 ships of 120 000 m^3 capacity capable of travelling at 18 knots is seen as a minimum.

Coppack[4] requoting and extending Peebles, points out that by the early 1980s LNG should be contributing about one eighth of the demand for all natural gas and about one thirtieth of the total demand for oil and gas together. However, the capital investment for LNG is about double that for an equivalent amount of energy in the form of oil, and to ensure the developments considered as possible by Peebles would require an investment of $40 billion (10^9) in the next 10 years.

The present author accepts many of the limiting factors described by Peebles and by Coppack, and in presenting Figs. 1 and 2, which summarise the possible development of an inter-regional transfer of gas by 1977 and 1981, has included all considerations other than those which assume that the various parties concerned are unwilling to come to any sort of commercial agreement.

SUMMARY

The future growth of natural gas is assured. It will stem in part from substitution for other fossil fuels and partly because of the continuing economic and industrial growth in the main areas of consumption and the demands for sulphur-free fuels.

The main advantages of natural gas to the consumer are its versatility, and the relative cleanliness of the products of its combustion in a society

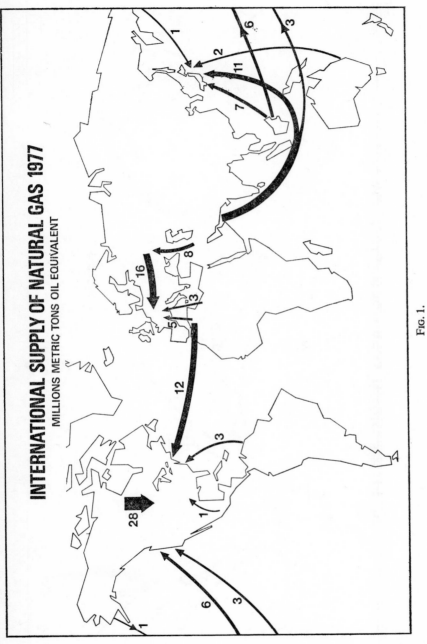

INTERNATIONAL SUPPLY OF NATURAL GAS 1977
MILLIONS METRIC TONS OIL EQUIVALENT

Fig. 1.

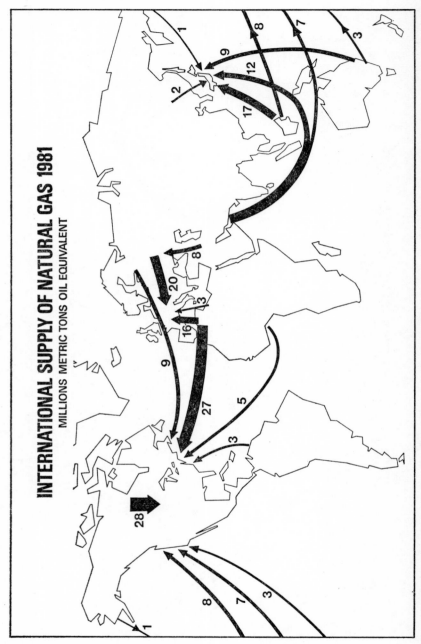

INTERNATIONAL SUPPLY OF NATURAL GAS 1981
MILLIONS METRIC TONS OIL EQUIVALENT

increasingly conscious of environmental problems. In a world where cheap oil is a thing of the past and where nuclear energy is unlikely to make a significant impact in this decade, the opportunities for developing the use of natural gas are highly encouraging. In the USSR reserves appear to be more than sufficient to meet indigenous requirements, but in the main energy-consuming markets of the USA, Japan and Europe the development of natural gas will be affected by limitations of supply rather than of demand. These supply constraints should result in more selective uses of natural gas, which in turn will place a premium value on its use as a high quality product.

In the continuing search for and development of indigenous reserves located near large energy markets we may expect to see production from onshore and from undersea reserves of both non-associated and associated gas. It must, however, be emphasised that the costs and the risks inherent in this kind of exploration and development, particularly in offshore areas, call for adequate recognition in terms of market price.

The main growth in natural gas consumption will derive from the utilisation of gas reserves located in areas remote from the main consuming areas. This will involve a dynamic growth in the LNG industry which, again, can only be achieved by large financial and technical investment in the construction of liquefaction plants, LNG tankers and reception and regasification facilities.

The capital required for the promotion of an LNG project, involving the production, gathering and liquefaction of gas, its movement over several thousands of miles of ocean by specially designed and constructed tankers and its final reception, storage and regasification, is high as compared with that required for the injection into the market of similar quantity of energy in other forms. This extra capital investment must be reflected in the ultimate price for gas. For this reason, in an international and competitive market, LNG supplies to Europe in the short and medium term are likely to be confined to those from North Africa, as the finally emerging price in schemes involving gas from more distant areas is likely to be less attractive to European gas distributors than to US and Japanese ones. However, in the longer term, when gas has established a full international role, gas from all areas will be fully integrated into the global supply of energy.

REFERENCES

1. P. F. Corbett and T. F. Gaskell (1968). 'Natural gas: sources, availability and markets', Institute of Fuel Conference, Eastbourne.
2. H. R. Warman (1972). 'The future of oil', *Geographical J.*, **138**(3), 287–92.
3. M. W. H. Peebles (1972). 'LNG trade in the 1980s', LNG-3 Conference, Washington.
4. C. P. Coppack (1973). 'Developments in LNG', 12th World Gas Conference, Nice.

Discussion

Professor A. Williams (University of Leeds): In 1968 I presented a paper at a conference called 'Natural Gas in the 1980s', and in this paper I suggested that a figure of 18% would represent the share of the UK energy market in the 1980s held by natural gas. Some of B.P.'s marketers recently told me that this figure was unduly pessimistic. Would you care to comment?

Mr J. G. Stainer: It is very difficult to be specific on a figure of this sort. I mentioned in the paper that in order to sustain supplies to the UK market after the middle and latter 1970s, gas from the Northerly fields would probably need to be tapped and higher prices required to encourage the opening up of these fields. So inevitably in any forecast of this sort, there is some sort of assumption on price. Having made that point, I cannot say with a great deal of accuracy what the assumption on price is but it is very much dependent on the economic climate.

Mr J. A. Nowill (Shell-Mex and B.P.): Following Professor Williams' question, I noticed in Table 5 that the UK advance for 1971 to 1980 is 50 m tons of oil equivalent. Now that is significantly greater than in Japan in Table 1. This seems rather surprising in view of what you have said concerning the natural gas imports into Japan from various sources. Secondly, you said that you are postulating this increase of natural gas in the UK to the northern fields. Surely it must be rather more than postulation, there must be some definite fact there?

Mr. J. G. Stainer: I will answer your second question first. Indeed we are assuming that the gas will be delivered. As far as the relationship between Japan and UK is concerned, in Japan we are really making a forecast of the rate at which LNG schemes will be mounted. LNG schemes take at least five years, and probably seven years to develop, so it is a matter of speculation as to whether we can argue that LNG schemes which are just now beginning to get off the ground will contribute very much to the Japanese supply by the end of this decade. They will come in at about 1979 or 1980. In terms of LNG imports, it is much easier to talk of predictions for say 1985.

Professor P. R. Odell (Erasmus University, Rotterdam):
Price of North Sea gas
As most of this will be associated gas why must it have a higher supply price than other North Sea gas. As it is a joint product with oil—and oil is the objective of the search—the associated gas in theory has a *zero* cost at the well-head. Its *supply price* could, therefore, be as low as is necessary to cover transport costs to markets.

Mr J. G. Stainer: Not all new Northern gas sources are associated. Your comments on associated gas are probably justified—but only just. Price depends very much on how one proposes to bring the gas ashore and the effect of associated gas production on oil production rates. Each affects costs. As far as unassociated gas is concerned, I do not think there is any doubt but that a higher price than is currently prevailing in the Southern part of the North Sea must be secured to make the exploitation of the gas worthwhile.

Professor P. R. Odell:

Western European reserves

Currently 5200×10^9 m^3—exclude associated gas in the North Sea. A reasonable hypothesis for 1980 reserves figure is $10\,000 \times 10^9$ m^3—Corbett's paper indicates a Western European gas consumption of 280×10^9 m^3 which excluding the effect of imports of about 30×10^9 m^3 gives a 50-year reserves/production ratio—or several times the normal oil industry figure for depleting gas fields in demand centres. Why? Will there be a supply limitation by the producers? Will the sellers (*e.g.* Gas Corporation) not be able to sell the gas? Will the infrastructure not be developed? Or do Europeans not like gas?

Mr J. G. Stainer: Well, I have to be honest with you, I cannot answer that question. I do not know if Dr Gaskell can throw any light on this?

Dr Gaskell (British Petroleum Co. Ltd): I am quite certain that any oil company that has got an oil field with any associated gas to spare would be pleased enough to have the Gas Council buy at well-head, and pipe it ashore themselves. The Gas Council though, do not want to do that I understand, they want it produced at shore lines for them at the sort of price that they are paying for the gas in the south. In the States with the Federal gas pricing they found that people did not want to go into the business of looking for gas alone. To get people to look for more gas alone, in the North Sea, you have got to put the price up.

Mr H. Lucas (Lucas Petroleum (UK) Inc.): We can back up Dr Gaskell. Our regulations in the USA have caused a shortage. Years ago in projections there was no shortage. I would wonder how Professor Odell plans to finance the dry holes.

Mr M. W. Clegg (British Petroleum Co. Ltd): In response to Professor Odell's comments I would like to point out that:

a. It is unrealistic and infeasible to have production facilities developed to, say, a reserves/production ratio of 20:1 concurrently with the proving of the reserves (estimated by Odell to be doubled for the North Sea/Europe by 1980). There must be delay-time of three to four years between proving of reserves and establishment of production.

b. The production of associated gas is determined by the rate of *oil* production—so that the total gas potential in Europe will depend upon the relative proportions of associated and non-associated gas.

Miss M. P. Doyle (Esso Petroleum Co. Ltd): My question arises from Professor Odell's statement that there was no reason to forecast a need for higher prices to bring in large quantities of new gas from the North Sea because associated gas had zero cost.

Energy prices, whether for oil, gas or coal depend on supply and demand and the possible availability of satisfactory substitutes. Regardless of who owns the North Sea reserves their price to the consumer will be determined by *world* prices. Willingness of the German Consortium to pay high prices for Ekofisk, has demonstrated to the British Gas Corporation that future gas supplies in the UK are likely to be at levels determined by the value that other consumers place on these supplies. The idea of zero-cost associated gas can in no way determine future prices.

Mr J. M. C. Bishop (Philips Petroleum Co. Ltd): I would like to make just one comment. It is not necessarily true to say that the Germans were prepared to pay more than the Gas Council for Ekofisk gas, there were many other factors involved in the choice as to where Ekofisk gas should go. I must dispute Professor Odell's statement that associated gas is a free benefit arising out of oil production. First, associated gas complicates field development and production. If you sell the gas you can no longer use the economic optimum method for oil production. If your fields are a long way off-shore you could well decide, for oil alone, to adopt off-shore loading on a long term basis. Associated gas, however, forces one to build a crude pipeline effectively as a gas facility to ensure supply continuity. Also, of course, you must build the gas pipeline. This accumulated capital investment attributable to associated gas makes it far from a free side benefit.

Mr Broadbent (National Coal Board): In the coal industry we have associated gas too—we call it methane. We grade it and we sell it, and we find exactly the same thing, that it is the cost of the pipelines and facilities to drain it, to get it away. You are really bringing up the marginal cost theory. Our coal that we find by open-cast method is cheaper coal than deep mined, but we still sell it at the standard rate.

Mr G. A. Hogg (British Petroleum Co. Ltd): There is one other important factor which has not, I think, been touched upon and which can make a big difference in the economics of bringing associated gas ashore by comparison with the economics of non-associated gas. This is the pressure at which associated gas is available, which is governed by well-head pressures and consequently separator pressures, which are normally much less than those for gas fields. To bring this associated gas ashore from considerable distances would need large amounts of costly off-shore compression.

As an example, the planned long term separator pressure for the Forties field is of the order of 50 psig.

Mr J. G. Mills (Lindsey Oil Refinery): In view of the demand for total energy required by Japan, what are the possibilities for discovering and developing natural gas supplies from China. Are these sources likely to be competitive with those of the USSR in the next ten years?

Mr J. G. Stainer: I think there is a very good chance of a gas supply arrangement being developed between China and Japan. Political relations between the countries over the last few recent years have improved enormously and are certainly of a sufficiently friendly nature now to permit a long term gas supply arrangement of this sort. It is doubtful that any supplies from China will be by pipeline, and it is more probable that there will be a liquefaction scheme associated with delivery. In view of the long lead time it is unlikely therefore supplies will start to flow before the end of the decade.

Mr B. A. Nolan (Irish Shell and B.P. Ltd): Before leaving the question of sources and levels of supply of oil and natural gas, would the speaker or Dr Gaskell care to comment on the prospects of supply from Siberia to the US West Coast and/or Japan since the logistics appear to be favourable and the political possibilities improving.

Mr J. G. Stainer: I think the prospects are very good. The gas is quite clearly there, and as I am sure you know, there has been considerable activity over the last few years to mount schemes to exploit it. I think the probability is, that in so far as the schemes get off the ground, and again it is a long lead time—1500–2000 miles of pipelines associated with it—the probability is Japan will be likely to benefit before anybody else. There is also in the longer-term, the possibility of supplies not only to the West coast of the United States but also to the East coast. Here I think we are up against the political uncertainties. I understand from my American colleagues that although the practicalities of such a movement have been explored in some considerable details now, the political climate necessary to enable such a scheme to go forward has not yet been created. Whether it will be created within the next five or six years I think is debatable, but depending upon the acuteness of the US gas shortage I think the prospects of a Russian/US gas deal in let us say the early or mid-1980s, is a very real one.

Dr Gaskell: The only point I would add is that Siberia is a large area of sedimentary rock. If you take the view that when you are looking for deep oil or gas fields you cannot follow the old fashioned method of looking for surface indications, and that any thick large sedimentary area is a potential oil or gas area, then Siberia must contain a large quantity of oil and gas. The present indications of drilling are that this is so. So, whether the Russians will want to go in for long distance pipelines and gain capital by exporting their materials, or whether they will want to grow personally rich by using it themselves, and getting their energy standards up to the same sort of rate that the US has been enjoying for some years, or whether they will take an ideological stand-point and use the gas to supply under-developed or developing countries, I do not know. But from the geological or geophysical point of view it looks a very promising area because it is a large tract of sediment and it is very thick.

Mr N. White (Hambros Bank): I wonder whether the speakers would care to extrapolate a little beyond the 1980s in regard to substitute fuels for natural gas? I wonder if Mr Stainer would care to comment on how synthetic natural gas, particularly in the US, is likely to fare in the longer-term future, and also the transportation of methanol, as an alternative to LNG from overseas.

Mr J. G. Stainer: Indeed, the USA is a particularly good example to take for this purpose. We think that LNG although expensive might not continue to be so very much more expensive compared with the conventional fuels, as it is at the moment. To give you some indication and some figures on this, it appears that LNG into the US on the East coast is going to lay down from now on at something in the order of $1·20 per million Btu's depending where it comes from, it could be $1·50, it is in that order. This equates to something like 8 or 9 dollars per barrel of fuel oil, and as you probably know, low sulphur fuel oil currently reaches the US East coast for something in excess of 5 dollars per barrel. Now, the LNG prices I am quoting ($1·20–$1·50) are really end of the decade prices. One must add on the effect of inflation, of OPEC Government take, etc. to the fuel oil prices to get a fair comparison. I do not think that many people would dispute that the low-sulphur fuel oil price of say $8 or $9 per barrel by the end of the decade is all that unlikely. So the disparity with low-sulphur fuel oil probably is not as great as it appears to be at present. As far as synthetic gases are concerned, one reads many articles with various estimates of the likely price of the gas, but here again we are talking basically in terms of $1·20 or more for synthetic gas, and more particularly this is usually based on a naphtha gas supply which is probably even more uncertain than either the LNG or fuel oil supplies. Now methanol or methyl alcohol is really nothing more than a means of circumventing the exceedingly high costs of LNG transportation, and although liquefaction itself is an expensive operation the shipping of LNG is exceedingly expensive in comparison with any other form of transportation. Methanol could be moved in conventional or very near conventional tankers, but the process of manufacturing the methanol from natural gas is more expensive than liquefaction into LNG. I do not think methanol in itself offers any intrinsic advantages over LNG. Calculations done so far suggest that the distance between the supply source and the market should be something over 5 thousand miles one way before methanol became a more economic proposition than LNG. This means that methanol is likely to give the USA access to Middle East supplies of natural gas much quicker than LNG would. In fact I think there has already been an announcement in the last week or two of a methanol deal based upon Persian Gulf supplies to the US. The role of methanol in the market place depends very much upon the sort of market that one is dealing with. I think it is quite possible that methanol could be used in Japan, and if it were the probability is that it would go to direct burning. In the USA the probability is that the demand for methanol will come not from power stations normally burning, for example, low-sulphur fuel but from the gas transmission companies who have an existing and elaborate gas transmission network, which they need to fill with gas.

Mr G. F. Skelton (formerly with British Petroleum Co. Ltd): With regard to the availability of associated gas it should be remembered that some regulatory bodies— for example the Alberta Oil and Gas Conservation Board—require that the produced gas be re-injected in order to conserve the reservoir energy required to produce the associated oil.

This requirement applies particularly where pressure maintenance by the alternative method of water injection is impracticable or uneconomic.

Mr P. G. Robinson (Davy Powergas Ltd): I would like to offer a comment on Mr White's question on the prospects for SNG in the USA. President Nixon's 'energy message' is now interpreted, I believe, as meaning that US companies will be exempt from tax on imported supplies only if at least 50% of the oil is produced as petrochemical feedstocks. This puts the gas companies, who will be relying on imported naphtha for example as their SNG feedstock, at a serious disadvantage and makes the short-term prospects for SNG rather bleak.

Mr J. G. Stainer: I would like to add one point. I have probably overlooked the most important aspect of the US energy situation. With their reserves of coal, in the long-term there is little doubt that their gas supplies will stem from coal gasification; but this again is a very expensive operation and tends to produce lean gas and the probability is that we are talking in terms of a price of something well above $1·50 by the end of the 1970s.

CHAPTER 5

Nuclear Energy 1: An Effective Competitor

D. C. LESLIE

Professor of Nuclear Engineering, Queen Mary College, University of London, UK

THE RESOURCES BASE FOR FISSION POWER

The $Q = 10^{18}$ Btu is a convenient unit for discussing world energy consumption. It is equivalent to 25 billion (10^9) tonnes of oil, or to about 200 billion barrels. Present world consumption is about $\frac{1}{4}$ Q/yr, and this is expected to rise to between 1 Q/yr and 2 Q/yr by the year 2000. Indeed, it seems certain to reach the lower figure unless our economic system collapses, since adjustment to a lower level of energy consumption can hardly be made in a shorter time. Even the lower figure implies a total consumption between now and 2000 AD of about 15 Q.

The total solar input to the earth is about 5200 Q/yr, and of this about 1200 Q/yr enters the hydrological cycle. Many people expect that if our energy consumption reached 1 % of the latter figure—say 10 Q/yr—we might seriously alter the world's climate. If this is right, consumption must flatten off in the first half of the twenty-first century, and 1 Q/yr seems a good figure for long-term planning: it implies that in the long-term the human race will show a certain abstemiousness, either in consumption or in population.

TABLE 1
The World's Reserves of Fossil Energy

Liquid oil	7 Q (King Hubbert low)
	to
	11 Q (King Hubbert high)
Natural Gas	10 Q
Tar sands and oil shales	30 Q
Coal	200 Q (very approximate)

Table 1 summarises the world's reserves of fossil energy. Contrasting these figures with those in the previous paragraphs confirms that there is every reason to be concerned about the supplies of liquid oil. Hydrocarbon fuel supplies will last into the twenty-second century and perhaps beyond, but they seem certain to be very expensive.

The only substantial, currently available alternative to these hydrocarbons is uranium (with thorium as a backup material). I shall be discussing the prospects for fusion in my second lecture: for this lecture, it suffices to say that this technology has not yet been invented. It seems most unlikely that either tidal or hydro power can make any appreciable contribution. Solar energy seems a good way of heating buildings, but I am doubtful about it as a source of concentrated, high temperature energy.

While oil has a unique worth of 25 billion tonnes = 1 Q, the energy worth of natural uranium (as it comes from the ground) depends on what you do with it: the position is summarised in Table 2. It is evident that uranium is a

TABLE 2

Energy Value of Uranium

Total fission	1 Q =	12 000 tonnes
Used in a fast reactor	1 Q_f =	25 000 tonnes
Used in an enriched thermal reactor	1 Q_{th} =	600 000 tonnes

very concentrated form of energy, even when it is badly used in a thermal reactor. Incidentally, when natural uranium is passed through a thermal reactor the 98 % of its potential energy content which remains unused is not ruined—about half of this 98 % can still be extracted in a fast reactor.

Table 3 shows some recent estimates of available deposits. These were an

TABLE 3

Estimates of Uranium Deposits

High-grade (less than $10/lb)[1]	1·5 Q_{th}
Medium-grade ($10 to $80/lb)[2]	30 Q_{th}

accurate statement of what was known when the various estimates were prepared, but, as we shall see, they must be a gross understatement of how much is actually available. One's first reaction to this Table is that it is hardly worth bothering with nuclear power, since the total energy reserve appears to be little greater than that of liquid oil.

This reaction is a mistake, since Table 3 is based on the use of known deposits of uranium in thermal reactors. If this same quantity of uranium were used in fast reactors, the resource base would immediately expand to 800 Q_f. Adding in the known deposits of thorium, the known reserves of fissile energy are in excess of 1000 Q_f. This is considerably greater than the total reserves of fossil energy, and justifies the effort now being devoted to nuclear power.

The proper deduction from Table 3 is that there is no immediate need for the fast reactor. Even if the nuclear contribution amounts to ½ Q/yr by the year 2000, this energy could be provided by thermal reactors without putting undue pressure on uranium resources. (Such a contribution would imply a world nuclear electrical capacity of 33 million MW at 50% load factor, and it seems unlikely that we shall reach such a figure.) The costing in section

2 is based on a uranium price of \$8/lb (of U_3O_8). If this price were increased 10-fold to \$80/lb, the price of electricity from a thermal reactor would double. My guess is that at even this high ore price, nuclear electricity will still be much cheaper than electricity from oil in the year 2000. This is important. The technology of fast reactors is difficult, and I shall be arguing in my second lecture that we shall save ourselves a lot of grief and expense if we introduce it rather slowly. Even this enlarged figure of 1000 Q_f gives no real picture of the extent of the fissile energy reserves. Uranium is not a rare element. Its average concentration in the earth's crust is about 2·8 ppm (by weight) so that the top km of the continental crust contains about

$$10^{12} \text{ tonnes} = 1·5 \times 10^6 Q_{th} = 4 \times 10^7 Q_f$$

of uranium. It is the heat produced by the radioactive decay of this uranium, on a timescale much longer than that of the universe, which builds the mountains. In addition, thorium is potentially as good a fuel as uranium, and is three times as abundant.

Therefore if we can use all the fissile material, it will last us for something like 100 million years. This isn't eternity, but it is so long that it makes no sense to worry about what will happen when the material is all used up. It is more reasonable to be concerned about the fraction of this potential wealth which can be found and used. The disparity between the estimates in Table 3 and the figures I have just quoted is very striking. It arises because attention has so far been concentrated on ores which are both high grade and relatively easy to find. In future we must put more effort into prospecting, and we shall have to use lower-grade ores. Both these measures imply higher uranium prices, and at some stage uranium may get too expensive to use in thermal reactors. However, there seems to be no risk of this happening in the present century.

If searches on land prove less rewarding then we expect, the sea contains 3×10^{-3} ppm of uranium (by weight), and its total content is roughly

$$3 \times 10^9 \text{ tonnes} = 4500 Q_{th} = 120\,000 Q_f$$

While small compared to the reserves in the rocks, this is still large, and it is accessible. Processes already proved on the pilot plant scale will produce uranium from seawater at \$80/lb or less.

Thus, while the question of energy supply provides us with many anxieties, the adequacy of fissile material supplies is not one of them. However, we do need to maintain a good effort in prospecting, mining and extraction.

IS NUCLEAR POWER NOW COMPETITIVE WITH OIL?

Because of uncertainties in costs, there can be no unique answer to this question. Unhappily, it is the two most important quantities which are the most uncertain. An oil-fired station committed now will start to need oil in 1977 or 1978, and the price which will have to be paid for this oil is really a matter of guesswork. I shall suppose that the station is designed to burn black oil, which powers a conventional steam turbine. (The gas turbine is only attractive at very low load factors.) I shall consider a range of prices from

$3.0 to $7.0/brl, delivered at the station: you can judge better than I can whether these figures are realistic. They are equivalent to

$$2\cdot18p/\text{therm to } 5\cdot08p/\text{therm}$$

or, at a net thermal efficiency of 40%, to

$$0\cdot186p/\text{uso to } 0\cdot433p/\text{uso}$$

(uso = unit sent out from the station).

The capital cost of a nuclear power station is also rather uncertain (particularly if one is outside the main organisations of the nuclear industry) but it seems likely that the tender price for a station ordered now in this country would be somewhere between £120/kWE and £200/kWE: I shall have more to say about these figures later on. With customer's 'on-costs' (additional expenses incurred by the CEGB, such as land acquisition and bringing roads and power lines to the site) at 10%, and interest at 10% pa during a 6-year construction period, the accumulated capital cost when the station comes on power is in the range

$$£153/\text{kWE to } £255/\text{kWE}$$

With a 25-year life, interest at 10% pa as before, and a discounted average load factor of 65%, the capital charges lie in the range

$$0\cdot297p/\text{uso to } 0\cdot494p/\text{uso}$$

In addition to inferring construction charges, we have had to postulate values for the interest rate, the average load factor and the nominal lifetime of the station.

The interest rate is much the most uncertain of these quantities, since it is really quite arbitrary. 10% pa seems to be the going rate for these calculations at the moment, but this figure could change at any moment. With an interest rate as high as this, the generation cost is very insensitive to the assumed lifetime, and the average load factor is mainly determined by usage during the first few years of the station's life.

The capital cost of the oil station and the fuel cost of the nuclear station are much better known. Oil-fired stations have recently been tendered to the CEGB and to the North of Scotland Hydro Board. For example, the Peterhead station was tendered to the NSHB at around £76/kWE.[3] With interest at 10% pa as before, a 4-year construction period, a 30-year life and an average load factor of 65%, this is equivalent to a capital charge of

$$0\cdot181p/\text{uso}$$

Fuelling a nuclear power station is a much more complex business than fuelling an oil-fired station. One has first to buy natural uranium. This contains only 0·71% of the fissile isotope U-235, which is insufficient for most reactors. One has then to pay for the U-235 concentration to be increased to whatever value one's reactor may need. This process is known as enrichment, and the U-235 concentration demanded by most of the reactors now built or building is between 2 and 3%. After enrichment the fuel has to be fabricated, a process which includes both shaping and canning. Finally, the spent fuel must be processed to recover the plutonium and to dispose of the wastes.

Published information is sufficient to determine the cost of all these processes with fair accuracy. The total fuel cycle cost (the usual term of art for the sum of all these costs) proves to be somewhat less than 0·10p/uso. I shall take this figure as the fuel cost of the nuclear station, so as to make some allowance for inflation and for uncertainties. This cost is divided almost equally between cost of natural uranium, cost of enrichment and cost of fabrication and processing. We are now in a position to compare the generating costs of the nuclear and the oil-fired stations, and this comparison is shown in Table 4. To me this Table says that, if nuclear is not competitive

TABLE 4

Comparative Costs of Nuclear Power and Oil

	Oil	Nuclear
Low	0·367p/uso	0·397p/uso
High	0·614p/uso	0·594p/uso

now, it must become so very soon. Since oil has many other uses and is soon going to be scarce, while uranium is abundant and isn't useful for anything else, one should surely start building nuclear stations and stop building high- or mid-merit oil stations. (I think there will be a place for gas turbine peak loppers for a long time to come.)

I should like to make two points about this comparison. The first is that nuclear power is very insensitive to the price of uranium ore. If this price were to rise tenfold from its present level of $8/lb of U_3O_8, the (low) cost of nuclear electricity would go up to around 0·7p/uso. (This assumes centrifuge separation, so that the cost of enrichment is insensitive to the price of energy.) In contrast, if oil prices increase tenfold from the assumed (low) figure of $3·0/brl, electricity costs will go up to over 2·0p/uso. This figure seems to me a not unfair measure of what we risk by continuing to build oil-fired stations of base-load type.

The other and even more important point is that this comparison is, in my view, cripplingly unfair to nuclear power with its high capital cost and low fuel cost. There is no precedent in modern times for an interest rate of 10%. It is the concomitant of a rate of inflation which has not been seen in the Western world since the Black Death. Perhaps half this interest is a true payment for borrowed money. The remainder is an allowance for the inflation of capital values. The unfairness and distortion comes in because no allowance is made for the inflation of the earnings. In the case of a power station, one would say that no allowance is made for increases in the cost of electricity after the station is commissioned.

The result of this lopsided method of accounting is that any capital-intensive project looks unaffordably expensive until one has actually bought it: once one has done so, it looks like a knock-down bargain. This process was very evident in the house market, even before it went crazy. It can also be seen in the CEGB's accounts. The earlier magnox reactors are great lumbering things which might incur total capital charges of £350/kWE if one were to duplicate them today. A combination of low fuel costs and distorted accounting makes them appear to be the cheapest stations on the Board's network. It is my firm belief that a more sensible accounting convention would show that nuclear power is cheaper than oil now.

RELIABILITY

The reliability of nuclear power plants is not as good as it should be, but it is not as bad as the more horrific stories would suggest. We all know that any new technology gives trouble when it is first introduced. We also know that if it is both sensible and necessary, it can be made to come right. The 500 MW turbo-alternator sets of the CEGB are a good example. The very large investment in these sets and their very poor initial performance produced an alarm that spilled over into the popular press. A lot of hard and devoted work has been done, and those sets are now beginning to perform very well: that sort of success story doesn't make headlines. I am sure the oil industry can show many stories of the same kind.

The technology of nuclear (fission) reactors is rather different from anything we have done before, and it has special difficulties of its own, such as the need for remote handling and inspection. In addition, the cycle time of the learning process is very long. Corrosion problems can take 5 to 10 years to make their presence felt, and the dwell time of fuel in the reactor is of the same order. With hindsight, it is now obvious that bad teething troubles were inevitable. All the evidence is that nuclear power stations can and will be made to conform to the usually accepted standards of reliability.

To illustrate these perhaps over-general sentiments, we will take a look at two reactor systems. Magnox (natural uranium metal fuel, canned in magnesium alloy, cooled by CO_2 and moderated by graphite) is a solid, reliable, expensive system: the people in the CEGB who operate these reactors are very fond of them. Apart from initial teething troubles which are now of no significance, there have been two main difficulties with this reactor type. There have been a number of unrelated faults on ancillary equipment, due essentially to the natural but false assumption that this equipment was well understood and that effort should be concentrated on the reactor itself. These faults have been expensive, but they do not cast doubt on the long-term viability of the system.

The most serious difficulty with magnox reactors has been the discovery, after some years of operation, that mild steel components both in the reactor core and in the heat exchangers had been corroding at an unacceptable rate. These components are so small and so numerous that it would be uneconomic to replace them, and the only cure which has been found is to downrate the reactors in order to reduce the temperature of the coolant gas. The resultant loss of power varies from one reactor to another. The greatest loss is 25% (at Wylfa) and one station (Berkeley) has not needed to be downrated at all. The magnox reactors perform very well at their new nameplate ratings, and it seems likely that they will continue to do so for the rest of their nominal lives. If we were to build another magnox station, the corrosion difficulty could be avoided by using more suitable materials. This hypothetical station would undoubtedly be very expensive: there is also every reason to think that it would be very reliable.

The Canadian CANDU system presents a similar and perhaps more encouraging picture (Fig. 1). This system also uses natural uranium, a tactic which, at some cost, frees one from the caprices of the USAEC. The fuel is in the form of UO_2 canned in zirconium while the coolant, pressurised D_2O, is contained in pressure tubes: the moderator is D_2O at atmospheric pressure.

This system has many attractions, but its economics are critically dependent on incessant movements of the fuel inside the reactor while it is at power. At each movement, a fuelling machine must be coupled and then uncoupled to a channel containing heavy water at a temperature of nearly 300°C and a

FIG. 1.   CANDU.

pressure of 100 bar. When performed in the Douglas Point prototype, these manoeuvres led to massive and apparently unstaunchable losses of heavy water. Heavy water is expensive, and these losses seemed to make the economics of the system unattractive. Also, the prototype was something like seven years late in coming to full power.

Many of us, looking at this picture and largely unaware of the solid development work which was being done on the system, took a gloomy view of its prospects. We were, therefore, as surprised as we were delighted by the splendid performance of the first commercial station at Pickering. When completed, this station will contain 4 × 500 MWE reactors. The first reactor was built in 5¼ years, including 8 months of strikes, and came to full power 6 months after being completed. Its load factor during the first 13 months of its life was 72%. Unit 2 was completed in 4½ years (including another strike) and its load factor over the first 7 months was no less than 86%. This is proof positive that careful attention to detail in design, in construction and in operation brings the same reward in this field as it does in any branch of engineering.

I am sure you will expect to hear something from me about AGR. The public image of this reactor has been dominated by the misfortunes of

Dungeness B. It is now generally agreed that these were exceptional, and that they were due to the contract being entrusted to an organisation which had neither the managerial nor the financial resources to carry it through. The experience with the other AGRs has been much better, even though it has not been all that we might have wished. It is hoped to have the first reactor of the second AGR station at Hinkley B on power this winter. If this is achieved, it will be 2 years late; in comparison with other reactor systems, this is by no means bad.

WHAT REACTOR TYPES ARE AVAILABLE NOW?

This question has a particular interest for the UK. We must start a new programme of nuclear power station construction soon, and we must decide what type to build. To the extent that it falls to any one man to make it, this decision will be made by Sir Arnold Weinstock: he can never have had a harder problem in his in-tray!

Only three reactor types are being sold today in the normal course of commerce. These are

CANDU, which we have already described
PWR (Pressurised Water Reactor)
BWR (Boiling Water Reactor)

PWR (Fig. 2) and BWR (Fig. 3) were both developed in the USA, and they are both gigantic nuclear kettles. PWR produces hot (light) water which is used to raise stream in a heat exchanger while BWR produces steam directly. In both reactors, the fuel is UO_2 canned in zirconium. I shall lump these two systems together though, if the choice were to fall on this pair, one would then have to decide which one preferred.

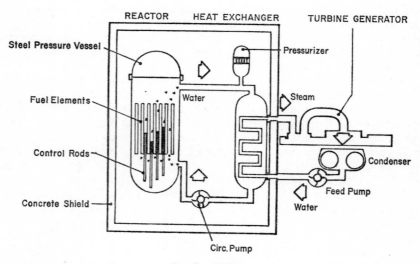

FIG. 2.   PWR.

WATER COOLED REACTORS

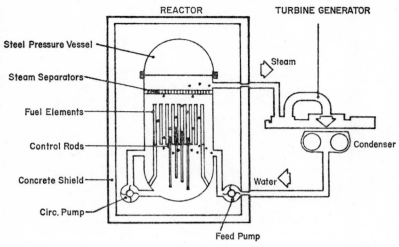

FIG. 3.   BWR.

British constructors are willing to tender two further reactor types now. These are AGR (Fig. 4) and SGHWR (Fig. 5). AGR is a development of magnox, with higher operating temperatures and pressures; the fuel is UO_2, canned in stainless steel. SGHWR is a sort of cross between CANDU and BWR. It is moderated by D_2O, but the coolant is boiling light water rather than pressurised heavy water. A natural uranium SGHWR can be built, but it has serious drawbacks and we in this country have never liked it much. The fuel of the British SGHWR contains about 2% of U-235, so that its enrichment is similar to that of PWR/BWR and of AGR.

GAS COOLED REACTORS

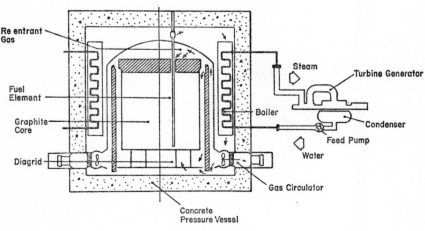

FIG. 4.   AGR.

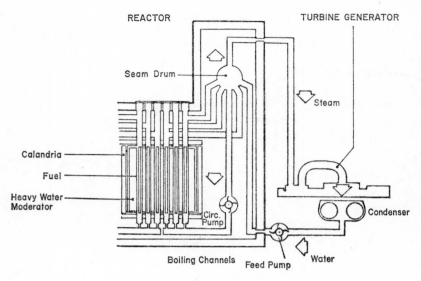

FIG. 5. SGHWR.

The other reactor type which must come into the British assessment is the High Temperature Reactor (HTR) (Fig. 6). This is the ultimate development of the gas-cooled line, with helium coolant and with no metal other than uranium in the core; graphite is used both as structural material and as canning. This reactor has immense attractions. It also has a number of development-type problems still outstanding, and the British Nuclear Construction Company will probably not be willing to tender it before 1975.

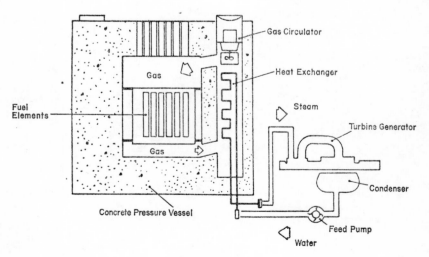

FIG. 6. HTR.

No other type of thermal reactor need be considered today, and I find it hard to imagine that any other type will ever come into widespread use.

I shall now enumerate the advantages and disadvantages of these various types. All types except CANDU require enriched fuel; the only bulk supplier of this commodity is the USAEC. The Commission has recently announced new terms, which many people think quite savage. These terms have encouraged both the Europeans and the Japanese to consider building large enrichment plants in a hurry. However, hurry is a relative term and the plants will be very expensive.

PWR/BWR

These types now dominate the world reactor market. There is much experience with them, and it ranges from the very satisfactory to the rather abysmal. As far as capital cost goes, these are probably the cheapest systems. They have recently been tendered in America at around £100/kWE, with dire warnings that this price will increase very substantially in the near future. Since American specifications are rather skimped by our standards, I assume that reactors of this type could be built in the UK from £120/kWE upwards, and this figure was used in our earlier assessment of the relative costs of oil and nuclear stations.

A furious controversy is now raging in the US about the safety of these types. It is fascinating as well as furious, and I am sorry that I have no time to explain it in detail. A general review is given by Wilson.[4] I don't think there is any need to question that the doubts now being voiced will be resolved, though the British position is that this must be done before we could commit ourselves to this system.[5] The real question is how much the additional measures which ensure safety will cost; if they include substantial downrating, the cost penalty could be severe.

The choice of this system would have many merits, not the least of which is that if there is trouble there will be plenty of people in it with us, all struggling to put it right. It would be naïve to suppose that this choice would give any sort of guarantee of perfect performance.

SGHWR

This choice would represent an intermediate position between going American and sticking to AGR. The general impression is that SGHWR is somewhat more expensive than PWR/BWR, but that the difference is not big enough to have much influence on the decision. The crucial arguments are

for   SGHWR is a home-grown product, and its safety is easier to demonstrate than that of the American reactors: indeed, it is probably not going too far to say that SGHWR is inherently safer. Load-following has been demonstrated, and the system is certainly valid for mid-merit stations.

against   Experience with this system is very limited, though the experience we do have is satisfactory. Also, if we make this choice we shall be more or less on our own, though the Canadians are interested in collaborating with us on this system.

CANDU

This system is not on the UK's shopping list, but perhaps it should be. As I have already said, experience with it so far is dazzling. Its safety is comparable with that of SGHWR, and it doesn't need enriched uranium. Its great drawback is its high cost. The Argentine government has just accepted a Canadian-Italian tender for a 600 MWE CANDU (Rio Tercero) at a capital cost of £170/kWE, and I assume that a CANDU could be built in Britain for about this price. This assumption also figured in our earlier cost assessment. The cost differential between CANDU and (say) SGHWR is considerable, but if one makes this choice one doesn't have to find further large amounts of capital for a European separation plant.

AGR

The UK has sunk a great deal of money and effort in this system; so far, all we have had from it is a lot of trouble and no commercial electricity. However, the impression is gaining ground that we have more or less learnt how to build this type of reactor and that, if we were to continue with it, we shouldn't have too much trouble in the future. Everything else being equal, it always makes sense to continue with an existing line of development, and this one does lead to a plant with outstanding safety characteristics; in this crowded island, this factor could well be decisive.

Unhappily other things aren't equal, and the most significantly unequal things about this reactor are its cost and the lack of any commercial operating experience with it. AGR is an expensive and complex system; my impression is that its cost is not very different from that of CANDU (say £170/kWE), while it does not have CANDU's compensating advantage of not needing enriched uranium. The cost is not decisive by itself and I imagine that if one or two AGRs were now working well, we would opt for going on with this system. In fact, we cannot hope to have any substantial body of operating experience for another $2\frac{1}{2}$ years. If we take the plunge now, we shall do so without any firm assurance that the system will work. (Though the argument, that we have already sunk so much in this system that it has got to be made to work, is not unimpressive.)

If we decide to wait till the beginning of 1976, we run a rather serious risk of being short of nuclear electricity in the 80s. Moreover, by then HTR, which is just as safe as AGR and more attractive in almost every other way, should then be available as an alternative.

As you will see, there is no obvious best choice.

THE SHORT-TERM MARKET FOR NUCLEAR POWER

Between now and 1985 (the date suggested by the Institute as a suitable horizon for a short-term review) the market will be dominated by the demand for nuclear power stations. Nuclear ships may be coming into commercial service by the end of the period, but in money terms they will still represent a small market in 1985. The same is true of the demand for sources of radiation, and for nuclear process heat.

On the other hand, the market for nuclear power stations is beginning to look a bit like the market for oil. Oil and gas shortages in the USA show that we are on the threshold of a period in which the growth of your industry will no longer be set by the growth in demand. In future, the limits will be set by some combination of the following factors:

Physical and/or political limitation of supplies,
The difficulty of amassing the necessary capital,
The need for planning consents, and the time taken to get them.

It seems that the nuclear industry is rapidly getting into the same situation.

Professor Mandel, who is one of Europe's leading authorities on this question, suggests that by 1985 the world should be installing 95 GWE of new nuclear capacity each year.[6] At a capital cost of £160/kW (the mean of the figures used above), this implies an investment of $38 billion ($10^9$) in the stations alone, with a further substantial investment in the fuel cycle. Such sums are not small, even by the standards of your industry, and there is no certainty either that they can be found or that the nuclear industry will be capable of construction on such a scale in only 12 years time.

Present experience suggests that the severest limitation on the expansion of nuclear industry may well come from difficulties and delays in getting planning consents. We don't actually make as much mess as you do, but we seem to be more hedged around by restrictions. While not all of these are rational, an emotional background going back to Hiroshima makes them very comprehensible. Difficulties of this kind have already caused delays of as much as 3 years in the start-up of some nuclear plants in the USA. It seems fair to say that the future prosperity of the human race depends, amongst many other factors, on a reasonable and reasonably speedy resolution of the differences between the environmentalists and the nuclear industry.

The scene in this country is broadly similar to that in the world as a whole. However, we have the additional complication that we have still to reorganise our nuclear industry and to select a thermal reactor type. This process may well take 2 years, and we cannot place a new order until it has been completed. The prognosticators seem to be agreed that thereafter, we should come up to an installation rate of at least 5000 MWE/yr as soon as possible. This implies a total investment, in power stations and the fuel cycle, of £1000 million a year or more. I would guess that, though it won't be easy, we shall succeed in finding the money. It also seems likely that the British nuclear industry will be able to cope with this rate of construction. However, it may well not have much spare capacity for export orders in the period up to 1985, implying that export prospects should not influence our choice of reactor too much. Finally, I would not expect too much difficulty in finding sites or in obtaining planning consents during this period.

ENVIRONMENTAL ISSUES

In the time available, I can do no more than glance at the principal risks. The most worrying of these is the remote possibility of a major accident to a reactor, leading to a massive release of fission products. It is clear that an accident on this scale is very improbable; indeed, some proponents of AGR would say that it was impossible for this reactor. The general viewpoint is that we cannot quantify the risk, nor can we define the probable consequences of such an accident.

If you are hearing this statement for the first time, your initial reaction may well be that this state of affairs is quite unacceptable. If so, I would invite you to weigh this risk against the risks implied by a decision not to have nuclear power; these latter risks include cold, starvation and social chaos. You could also compare the risks of nuclear power with those that we cheerfully accept in everyday life. On past evidence, a tank of phosgene is a far more dangerous object than a nuclear power station. Think of the risks you accept, almost without thinking, every time you drive your car. Remember that you spend most of your life inside buildings, and that there is a finite risk of the ceiling falling on you. This risk is probably greater than that of a major accident to a power reactor. There is a greater, though still small, risk of a minor accident resulting in the release of (say) 1000 curies of iodine-131. In this and many other countries, nuclear power stations are sited so that all harm to the public can be avoided by a mixture of medication and temporary evacuation.

Technical solutions are either available or visible for the long-term storage of radioactive waste. However, there is a difficult choice to be made between total burial (as in a salt deposit) and long-term supervision. Workers at Harwell are inclined to prefer the latter choice, in spite of the possible burden on our descendants, because it does give one the chance to rectify the consequences of a mistake or an accident.

SUMMARY

(a) Known uranium reserves are more than sufficient for the rest of this century, and the total supply is enormous.

(b) Uncertainties in costs are so large that it is not clear whether nuclear power is now competitive with oil. With reasonable assumptions, the present-day cost difference between the two methods of electricity generation is small.

(c) This implies that, if oil prices increase in the way that most people expect, nuclear power will be clearly cheaper by 1985.

(d) Nuclear power stations conform to the normal pattern for the development of radically new equipment. They are rather unreliable to begin with, but with increasing experience their performance may be expected to reach a satisfactory standard.

(e) There are several viable types of thermal reactors, and no one type is clearly preferable to the rest. The selection of the reactor to be built in this country will be as difficult as it is important.

(f) There will be plenty of work for the nuclear industry, and the question is more whether it can cope with the expected workload.

REFERENCES

1. McKelvey and Duncan (1965). Paper 139 in Symposium on Fuel and Energy Economy; Amer. Chem. Soc., Detroit.
2. Mandel (1971). Paper A/Conf./P. 359 in Geneva Conference on the Peaceful Uses of Atomic Energy.
3. *The Times*, 31 March 1973.
4. R. Wilson (1973). 'The AEC and the loss of coolant accident', *Nature*, **241,** 317.
5. Mr Davies in the House of Commons, 8 August 1972.
6. Mandel (1971). *J. Brit. Nuclear Energy Soc.*, **12,** 11.

Discussion

Mr M. B. Bolt (National Coal Board): Professor Leslie said that uranium ore prices could rise by a factor of 10 and nuclear power costs would not rise significantly. Yet other advocates of nuclear power state that we need fast breeder reactors to keep uranium prices at a reasonable level. My two questions are:

(i) Do we need fast breeder reactors?

(ii) If we do, what doubling time do we need for the fast breeder to have any effect on uranium prices?

Professor D. C. Leslie: My own view is that if we go out and find the uranium we do not need much in the way of fast reactors in this century. There are people who disagree very strongly with this and it is only a point of view. I don't go much on this short doubling time story. For one thing I do not think it is really on—it is not compatible with a safe reactor. So we have got to do without it and that means finding the uranium. Once one goes beyond the end of this century one is so tied up with the level at which world consumption will level off, and what luck we have with fusion. I tried to do some sums to prepare myself to answer that very question and I decided I could not do any meaningful calculations. It all hinges on whether we find the uranium fairly quickly; if we do not we are very likely to have problems.

Mr K. A. D. Inglis (British Petroleum Co. Ltd): You stress the need to send a lot of explorers out with an awful lot of money. Is the established resource base reliable enough to justify your presumed extrapolation in terms of the ultimate resource base? Is there a very big question mark about this extension of the resource base?

Professor D. C. Leslie: The established resource base is not the same as the ultimate, and I don't think there is any question about the ultimate base. We just do know about crustal abundance and the fast reactor could, if we were really desperate, run on granite. But I think the first thing we can do if prospectors do not locate big new deposits is go back to the sea-water process which could provide very substantial amounts of uranium.

Mr P. G. Robinson (Davy Powergas Ltd): It is very encouraging to learn of British developments in nuclear technology, but is not this the same old story of the UK pioneering the industry but leaving the commercial exploitation to others? I believe Westinghouse have something like 22 export projects in hand with the LWR design. What market prospects does the UK have and what is being done to promote the scale of UK nuclear technology and plant?

81

Professor D. C. Leslie: We have made a number of mistakes, there is no doubt about that, and the main mistake is that we have left it rather too late to be sufficiently commercial. It has been a scientific adventure in this country, for just a bit longer than was really safe. And, in that time, it is not only the Americans, but also the West Germans who have made away with large parts of the market. I cannot see that we are very likely to sell a light water reactor at all, if we went that route. I do not think we are likely to sell an AGR because it looks expensive. I think we could sell an SGHW because a number of people are interested in it. The Italians and Japanese come to mind particularly, and the Canadians could be prepared to come into a joint marketing venture with us. I think I agree there are prospects as always just over the next hill; we did after all invent HTR. We still have a lot of technology in it, and might achieve substantial export sales there. On the fast reactor I think we are limited by how much plutonium is available.

Mr J. M. C. Bishop (Phillips Petroleum Co. Ltd): The paper stresses the problems associated with nuclear waste disposal. Also it was said that spent fuel elements from a thermal reactor could still be used as fuel for a fast reactor. From this it appears that fast reactors could help to solve the waste disposal problem. Does not this aspect alone justify giving a higher priority to the early development of fast reactors?

Professor D. C. Leslie: I think perhaps I have confused you here. The waste which has to be stored is made up of fission products, and it looks as though those cylinders have got to be stored for at least 1000 years. We might produce 700 a year by the year 2000. But to store the depleted U-238 that would come out of a thermal reactor is not a great problem—just a few tons a year at the most.

Mr J. M. C. Bishop: Does the fast reactor have the same sort of waste disposal problem as the thermal reactor?

Professor D. C. Leslie: Yes, it does.

Mr D. C. Ion (formerly with British Petroleum Co. Ltd): Present proved uranium reserves were found scientifically; there has been no recent real uranium exploration effort and there are undoubtedly many deposits of 'commercial' uranium ore to be found.

Professor D. C. Leslie: The deposits that we have found so far have been found by geiger counters, which is equivalent to oil seepage, which you can see on the surface. But now we have got to start looking for deep deposits and we want a theory, similar to that which you people have built up, about where to look.

Mr M. Beudel (Petroleum Press Service): How much of the estimated uranium reserves are in Western Europe?

Professor D. C. Leslie: Very little, some in France, some in Spain, a certain amount in the North of Scotland and there are some shales in Sweden that are just below the exploitable limit at the moment, but which I am sure will come in in this century. However, we have an awful lot of water round our coasts. Also, a lot of the uranium deposits are in places that are, in the medium-term, not likely to turn awkward—Canada and Australia in particular—and the transport cost is negligible.

Mr E. W. Lang (British Petroleum Co. Ltd): The British are all on their own as far as nuclear reactors are concerned. Virtually nobody else considers the Advanced Gas-

Cooled Reactor as a commercial proposition. Bearing in mind that the French did a lot of work on these reactors and then two years ago threw it all over and went for American light water reactors, why is Professor Leslie so sure that the British are right?

Professor D. C. Leslie: I wouldn't put it that way. The AGR's are there—we have built them—we have invested in the order of a thousand million pounds. They have got to be made to work. But I do not think we would ever have built them if only we had known. We would have gone for HTR, I am sure.

Mr N. White (Hambros Bank): You give a comparison of the costs of nuclear power and oil. Do these allow for the use of waste heat such as is practised in Scandinavia?

Professor D. C. Leslie: These are the UK costs but the fuel cycle costs are virtually international, and the capital costs do not seem to vary too much. They put no value whatever on the waste heat. I am dubious about district heating in the British environment, the load factors look very low. We can put nuclear power stations within two miles of a built-up area, and it is not absolutely impossible to have district heating here.

Mr E. W. Lang: Two oil companies have just announced a joint venture to develop and sell high temperature reactors. How do these reactors compare with other reactors? In Professor Leslie's opinion are these oil companies developing the right type of reactor for commercial success?

Professor D. C. Leslie: This is a very personal opinion; you will get about as many answers as there are people who ask questions. Yes, I think it is a very good reactor, and in the long-term it must be the winner among thermal reactors. It looks cheaper and it is environmentally easier too. I think Shell made a good investment. I do not know whether the price was right.

Mr C. L. Goodacre (Consultant): First, is there any merit in the American suggestion to shoot radio active waste *via* rockets into space, and so lose this material by dispersion into the Solar System? Secondly, is this a practical serious suggestion or not?

Professor D. C. Leslie: I don't think it is practical today. It is a very attractive idea particularly if you take the trouble to drop it into the sun. You have got to launch it, and that looks like being very expensive, and there is a risk of crash on take-off. You want to make sure that the capsule can survive the worst accident, or that you are prepared to accept the consequences if it is not so designed.

Professor P. R. Odell (Erasmus University, Rotterdam): A 10% interest rate is surely 'modest' not exortionate. What happens to the comparative cost of fission and conventional electricity using a 15–20% DCF rate of return requirement on the contrasting investment in the two systems.

Professor D. C. Leslie: I don't really think I can comment. I have no way of knowing what an interest rate should be. There certainly is an interest rate at which oil would be more attractive. If you have an interest rate of 500% per annum, almost any oil price has to be better than the nuclear one.

Every time one does an estimate about a nuclear power station, since the interest rate started to go up above 4%, they always look a bit too expensive to buy, but every time one buys them they seem a knock-down bargain and the higher the interest rate the more that will be true.

CHAPTER 6

Increased Efficiency of the Use of Energy Resources

H. J. ALKEMA and E. V. NEWLAND

Shell International Petroleum Co. Ltd, London, UK

INTRODUCTION

Growth of energy demand/limited resources

Over the last 50 years world demand for energy (excluding USSR, Eastern Europe and China) has increased from 16·5 mbdoe* to 72·5 mbdoe. The rate of growth during this period increased steadily from 1·5% pa in the 1920s to 5·5% pa in the 1960s and is currently approaching 6%. Up till some years ago this increase in the rate of growth (input) was accompanied by substantial improvements in efficiencies of the use of fossil fuels, consequently output increased at even higher rates. Such improvements do not take place any more, on the contrary in various applications efficiencies are decreasing. The future rate of growth of energy demand will reflect both a decline in the rate of growth of the efficiency of mature technologies and an increase in efficiency brought about by new technologies and market forces.

Growth has so far been sustained primarily by oil and gas and for the next 10 years also the expanding energy requirements of Western Europe, the USA and Japan will have to be met principally by oil imports. From the late 70s/early 80s onwards however, it is unlikely that oil production, though it may still increase, will be able to keep up with growth in energy demand. The growth of energy supply, and for that matter economic growth, can then be maintained only if adequate measures are taken now to develop other energy sources and to increase efficiency in the use of fossil fuels.

The waste problem

An analysis of the fossil fuel consumption in the US, Japan and Western Europe shows (Fig. 1) that about half of the total supply is wasted in the process of conversion of fuels into more convenient forms of energy and in transportation of energy. The reasons for these losses are the low inherent efficiency of power generation (steam turbines) and of transportation (internal combustion engines) and to a lesser extent efficiency losses in industrial processes and in domestic/commercial heating equipment. In addition,

* Million barrels a day oil equivalent.

85

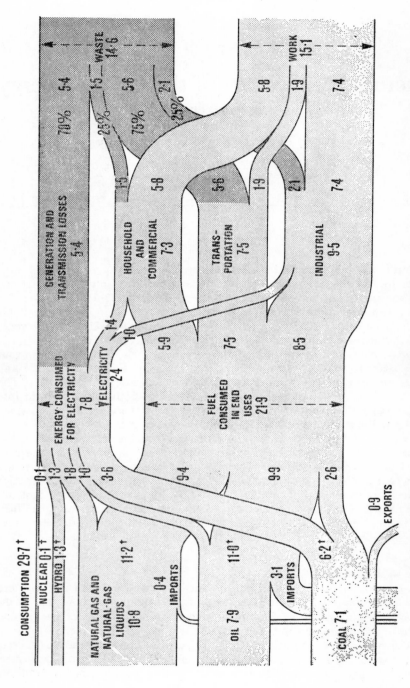

Fig. 1.   US flow of energy, 1970—million bdoe. Reproduced, by permission, from *Scientific American*, September 1971.

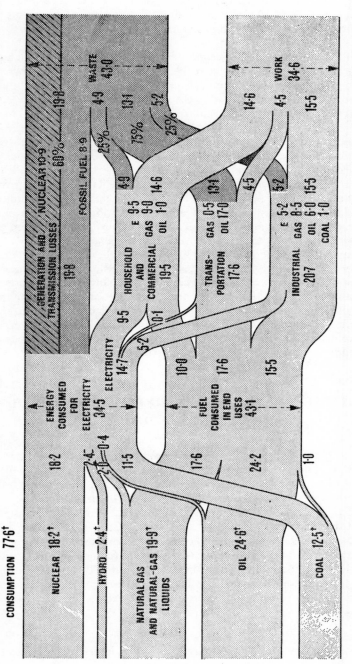

FIG. 2. US flow of energy, 2000—million bdoe. Reproduced by permission of The Mitre Corporation, July 30th 1971.

substantial avoidable losses are incurred in the use of energy, for example by insufficient insulation of buildings and inefficient uses of cars and other means of transportation (low load factors, non-regenerative braking, traffic congestion, etc.).

Against the background of the continued growth of demand for oil and gas and the growing concern about their future availability and cost, there is an increasing general interest in more efficient processes/technologies for energy conversion and in measures and methods to decrease wasteful use. This awareness of the waste problem is all the more justified since a 'surprise-free conventional-technology' projection (Fig. 2) of the energy consumption pattern does not show any improvement in the overall efficiency of fossil fuel consumption in this century. One of the main reasons for this is the increasing share of electricity in the total energy demand.

Where the growth of nuclear generating capacity will not meet the growth of electricity demand until perhaps well beyond 1990, this will mean continued growth of inefficient fossil-fuel-based power generation. (Of course present-day nuclear power generation is equally inefficient.) Moreover present trends in the transportation sector are towards lower efficiencies.

This paper discusses the scope and likelihood of the technological changes and government/industry actions that could possibly lead to increased efficiencies of the use of energy resources so as to change these 'surprise-free' projects and to buy the time needed for the transition to a predominantly nuclear-based energy abundant future. In the paper facts relevant to the US are frequently mentioned as it is believed that the problems now emerging in the US are likely to apply to most other major energy consuming areas in the years ahead.

POSSIBILITIES FOR THE INCREASED EFFICIENCY OF THE USE OF ENERGY RESOURCES

In July 1972, the Office of Emergency Preparedness (USA) finished their report for the Energy Sub Committee of the Domestic Council in which the impact of all possible technological improvements, tax and pricing policies, education and savings campaigns was estimated for the period up to 1990. The maximum effect of such measures would be very significant indeed (Fig. 3). Oil consumption would be down by 20% in 1980 and 25% in 1985 and 1990, saving 3·9, 6·2 and 7·5 mbd respectively. However, it was considered highly improbable that all these measures would (could) be taken and that they would all be successful. Therefore savings up to 30% of these estimates were considered more realistic. The most significant realisable measures to effect conservation of energy that were identified were:

Improved insulation in homes.
Development of more efficient air conditioning.
Shift of inter-city freight from highway to rail, inter-city passengers from air to ground travel and urban passengers to mass transit.
Introduction of more efficient industrial processes and equipment.

A more recent report of the Office of Emergency Preparedness issued in January 1973 discusses another possibility for energy conservation namely the substitution of a relatively abundant fuel for scarce fuels, more specifically the substitution of oil and gas by coal over the period 1973–1985. The maximum scope for oil saving by coal substitution in power stations was estimated to be 2 and 3 mbd by 1980 and 1985 respectively illustrating the potential importance of such substitution.

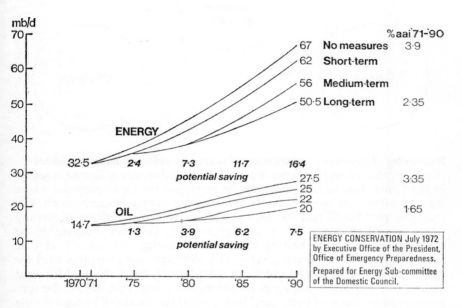

Fig. 3. Idealised projections of oil and energy demand in the US showing the *maximum* effect of conservation measures.

In this presentation we will not endeavour to go into the same depth as the OEP reports or to present similar results for Europe. We will try to develop the theme that anticipation of future developments should be guided by an awareness of limited resources; the potential high cost of energy; environmental constraints to future industrial and consumer activities; the time lag involved in any change; the high rate of growth of energy demand in terms of our capacity to discover and develop new resources; the increasing difficulty of financing energy growth; and most importantly, an awareness of the inherent conflict between low pollution, high efficiency and low cost.

It would seem that there is as yet no consensus of opinion about the most important basic facts. This presentation is a plea for more balanced thinking on these conflicting related subjects and the many possibilities for more efficient uses of energy resources will be discussed.

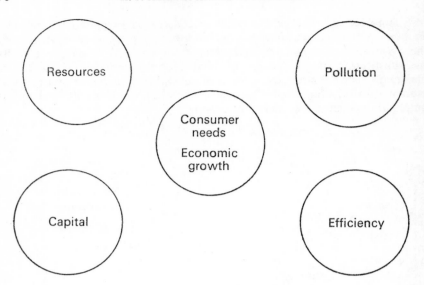

Re-routing of resources; substitution of scarce by more abundant resources

Accepting that oil and indigenous gas will be available only in limited amounts in the future they should preferably be employed for those purposes where they are either used most efficiently or where they hold a unique position. For example, gas should find its main market in domestic/commercial heating where overall efficiency can be as high as 70%. However, because of the seasonal nature of the heating market other outlets for gas will still be necessary for load balancing reasons. Oil, although also preferably used for direct heating purposes and chemicals manufacture, has to be used for road and air transportation as long as no alternative is available, despite the very low overall efficiency of these uses. Heavy fractions could still be used for the manufacture of bitumen and for peak load electricity generation, but the latter only in combined cycle installations (COGAS).

The simplified scheme in Fig. 4 shows an improved flow of energy from resources to consumers. For (abundant) coal two main applications are suggested: power generation and gas manufacture. There seems to be a strong case for maximum use of coal in power stations, particularly as processes for SO_2 removal from stack gas are available to prevent pollution which up till now, in addition to price, was one of the main reasons for a change away from coal in power generation. Gas manufacture from coal is considered a very likely development, particularly in the US, as one can envisage that the available quantities of natural gas and oil may not be sufficient to satisfy future demand in the domestic/commercial heating market.

To achieve maximum substitution new power stations should use coal extensively, as should existing power stations that can still burn coal. Oil and gas fired power stations should be converted or used as little as possible. The saving of oil and gas that can be achieved by substitution by coal is not easy to determine, as was shown by the OEP Study which arrived at the maximum saving for the US of 3 mbd by 1985. This study can be used as a guideline for similar studies for other countries. It is thought that the total world target for coal substitution for power stations is a saving of some 5 mbd by 1985. For this substitution some 400 million tons of coal pa would be needed.

Of course such developments would have a considerable effect on existing refinery practice, especially outside the US where additional facilities for conversion of the heavy end of the barrel to middle distillates and lighter fractions would have to be built. This would lead to increased cost for light products which one could consider as the price one should pay for this method of energy conservation.

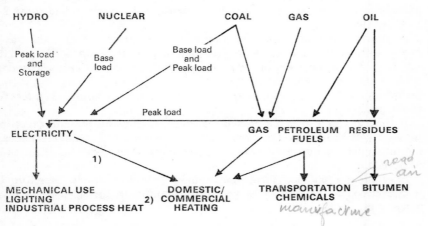

1) Limited application for smoothing daily load curves

2) If resulting in a higher overall quality/efficiency than the direct use of fossil fuels

FIG. 4.   Simplified flow of energy.

The use of resources that cannot be transported

In various parts of the world energy resources that cannot easily be moved to consumer areas have been discovered. In this category are large gas reserves (including associated gas in large oil producing areas) and hydropower potential. Although in principle one could set up enormous LNG schemes and perhaps methyl fuel and (electrolytic) hydrogen projects to transport these resources, the capital needs and the time required for such developments would seem to limit the scope of these possibilities in the near future.

An interesting alternative possibility would be to move the consumer to the resources. Excellent candidates for such moves are energy intensive industries such as base metal manufacture, in particular the aluminium and steel industries, uranium enrichment, refining and the manufacture of bulk chemicals.

Obviously many problems would be involved in such moves but provided that incentives and guarantees were agreed for such moves such developments might give a welcome contribution to the overall efficiency of the use of world resources.

Re-thinking of anti-pollution policies/measures

As mentioned earlier, there is often an inherent conflict between the result of anti-pollution measures and our aim to increase the efficiency of energy use. A notable example is transportation. Not only is transportation a very-low-efficiency area but recent anti-pollution measures in the US quite dramatically worsen the situation.

The introduction of high-octane non-leaded gasoline will result in a lower efficiency as additional refining losses are involved in its manufacture. Also exhaust gas purification is quite energy consuming. Estimates are that in the US gasoline consumption will go up by some 15–20% for this reason alone. Where by 1985 world gasoline consumption may be some 15 mbd (on today's efficiency) such measures, if introduced world-wide, might waste some 2–3 mbd by 1985.

In power generation the desulphurisation of either fuel or stack gas is energy consuming and estimates are that a loss of about 8% would be involved. The installation of peak-load gas turbines close to electricity consuming areas may be desirable from the anti-pollution viewpoint but it is an inefficient use of energy and, as already stated, it uses the wrong resources for power generation.

A third example is in the use of materials. If, for anti-pollution reasons, plastic materials for packaging were banned in favour of metal or glass packaging total energy consumption would increase (*see* later under Substitution of Materials, p. 99).

Existing and planned measures to fight pollution should therefore be re-considered and modified to give full attention to the need to increase efficiencies.

Electricity generation

In the long term nuclear power generation will take over virtually all generating capacity, thereby in the end helping to solve the fossil fuel resource problem. Nuclear power can then even be envisaged to be an abundant energy source that can be used for the manufacture of fuels such as hydrogen and methanol. Short term, however, nuclear capacity growth is not adequate to satisfy the growth of electricity demand so that at least up to 1990 additional fossil-fuel-based capacity has to be built. In the context of this paper this is clearly a negative trend because of the low efficiency of the use of this fossil fuel input.

In the area of fossil-fuel-based power generation new technologies are being developed to increase the overall efficiency, *e.g.* combined gas turbine/steam turbine installations (COGAS), fuel cells and magnetohydrodynamics. It is possible that such developments allow the efficiency of some new installations to be increased from some 38 to 45% by 1980, but this can only change the overall efficiency of the total generating grid by some 10% (relative).

Negative trends to counteract developments to higher efficiency are:

Anti-pollution measures (*see* previous section).
Capital shortages forcing excessive installation of low-efficiency gas turbine power stations where this should be limited to peak-load applications.

New generating capacity installed far from consumption areas and increasing delays in building.

In general one could say that present policies and developments do not reflect any expectation of a possible energy shortage, but only reflect low profitability and capital shortages in the industry together with an over-reaction to pollution problems. Developments that would seem desirable are:

Efficiency becoming as important a criterion as pollution, capital, etc.
High-efficiency technologies being pursued more vigorously.
Re-entry of coal.
Minimising the use of gas as fuel for power stations.
Crash nuclear programmes.
Power generation using household waste as fuel (*see* later under Electricity and Fuels from Waste, p. 99).

Waste heat of power stations (and other industrial plants)
The use of waste heat of power stations, if feasible, would indeed result in a significant overall saving of energy. Several solutions have been put forward such as district heating, greenhouse heating, and a combination of power stations with energy consuming industries. Such schemes have found limited applications because of high capital cost and difficulties to match the quality of rejected heat with needs of another industry. Where possible such schemes should of course be introduced. The fact that new sites for power stations are moving away from large population centres does however decrease the probability of district heating schemes. A potentially important development is the introduction of total energy systems especially designed to fit individual industries. It might be quite helpful if total energy systems were to be given economic support by paying such industries more for surplus electricity delivered to the grid. The possibility of circulating industrial cooling water to provide the heat source for domestic heat pumps would seem to merit further study.

Electricity demand
As has already been mentioned in the introduction, the share of electricity demand of total energy demand is increasing world-wide. This is because of many new applications for which electricity is being used in the household and because of increasing use in industrial processes.

Where a European family might use some 2000–5000 kWh per annum depending on the social class the family belongs to, the average consumption in the US is some 7500 kWh (including use for heating and cooling purposes) and it is considered possible than an all-electric home might consume some 25 000–30 000 kWh per annum by 1985. Without measures being taken to prevent such developments electricity demand in developed countries would rise much faster than energy demand.

The use of electricity for domestic/commercial heating purposes such as room heating, hot water, dish washer, washing machine, clothes drier, etc., is less than half as efficient as the use of fossil fuels (30 % efficiency as against some 70 % for gas or oil) if this electricity is produced from fossil fuels, which will be the case for a long time to come. It is therefore very important that the use of electricity for heat purposes be limited as far as possible. In fact it should only be advocated for smoothing daily load curves, which would limit the amount of electricity available for heating to some 10% of total production.

As was recently discussed at an Energy Policy Workshop sponsored by the MITRE Corporation and the Hudson Institute, governments could perhaps introduce an excise tax, the rate increasing with the amount of electricity used. Such a measure could indeed have a large impact on the growth of electricity demand.

It is of course highly desirable that when electricity is used it is used efficiently. Insulation of electrically heated buildings and improved efficiency of lighting are areas of importance in this context.

The RAND Corporation recently made some specific recommendations to reduce the growth of electricity demand in California that are in line with above comments:

> Substitution of gas for electricity in all new installations for space heating, cooking, refrigeration, air conditioning and water heating.
> Use of solar energy for space heating and other uses.
> Better thermal insulation of new buildings and homes.
> Construction of more 'low energy use' buildings.
> Reduction of the amount of electricity required for lighting.

Waste at the consumer end

The most promising area for increased efficiency of energy use is conversion and avoidance of waste of energy at the consumer end. The waste involved falls into two categories. Firstly there is the waste that is caused by efficiency limitations of the equipment used (*e.g.* boilers, engines and batteries) for conversion of fuels into heat, mechanical energy and electricity at the consumer end. This waste was shown in Fig. 1 as being 25% for household and commercial markets, 25% for the industrial market, and 75% for the transportation market. The second category of waste at the consumer end is the wasteful use of the energy produced, *e.g.* by insufficient insulation, by low load factors in transportation, etc. This waste was not shown in Fig. 1. For this discussion the two categories will be taken together looking at the three most important areas of waste: transportation, domestic/commercial heating and air conditioning, and industrial uses.

Transportation

Tables 1 and 2 illustrate the important contribution of transportation to total oil demand and the importance of road transportation within the transportation sector. Table 3 shows very low overall efficiencies obtained on the road with present internal combustion engine powered cars. It also shows the potential for improvement which lies in the development of other prime movers. Of course one should be aware of the enormous difficulties of development of a true competitor to the internal combustion engine in terms of cost, size and performance.

Rice[1,2] and Hirst[3,4] have for typical US conditions made comparisons of the actual efficiency of urban and inter-city passenger traffic and for inter-city freight transport (Table 2 taken from reference 3 and Tables 4, 5 and 6

TABLE 1
Contribution of Transportation to Oil Demand

	Western Europe		
	1970	1980	1985
Oil input (mbd)	13·2	22	26·5
Oil for transportation	3·5	5·8	7·4

	US		
	1970	1985	2000
Oil input (mbd)	11	28·5	24·5
Oil for transportation	7·5	13·5	17

TABLE 2
Distribution of Energy within the Transportation Sector in the US

	percentage of total energy	
	1960	1970
Automobiles	52·8	55·3
urban	25·2	28·9
inter city	27·6	26·4
Aircraft	3·3	7·5
Railroads	4·0	3·3
Trucks	19·9	21·1
inter city	6·1	5·8
other	13·8	15·3
Buses	0·7	0·5
Other	19·3	12·3

TABLE 3
Overall Passenger Car Efficiencies[a]

Type of power source	percentage
Internal combustion engine (rich)	10–14
(lean)	14–18
Diesel engine (small)	21
Rechargeable batteries (present electricity grid)	15–19
(45% efficiency of electricity generation)	19–24
Fuel cell (50–70% efficiency of the fuel cell)	21–34

[a] From primary fuel to actual useful energy on the road.

TABLE 4

Energy–Efficiency for Inter-city Passenger Traffic

	Passenger-miles/gallon	Btu/passenger-mile
Buses	125	1 090
Railroads	80	1 700
Automobiles	32	4 250
Aircraft	14	9 700

TABLE 5

Energy–Efficiency for Urban Passenger Traffic

	Vehicle-miles/gallon	Passengers/vehicle	Equivalent passenger-miles/gallon	Btu/passenger-mile
Bicycles			765	180
Walking			450	300
Buses	5·35	20·6	110	1 240
Automobiles	14·15	1·9	27	5 060

TABLE 6

Energy–Efficiency for Inter-city Freight Transport

	Ton-miles/gallon	Btu/ton-mile
Pipelines	300	450
Waterways	250	540
Railroads	200	680
Trucks	58	2 340
Aircraft	4	37 000

taken from reference 4). From these tables it follows that apart from the obvious advantages of using bicycles for short trips (in the US 55% of the trips are less than 5 miles and account for some 10% of total mileage) there must be scope for a shift away from cars to railroads and buses provided that indeed in practice higher passenger load efficiencies as implied in the tables will be achieved in these modes of transportation.

A conclusive analysis of the total transportation system for different countries seems overdue. This should include the establishment of basic needs for transport and of optimum vehicle type, manufacture, distribution and fuelling, and the provision of roadways, parking, servicing and vehicle disposal. All of these functions are energy related and are likely to have a bearing on any attempt to limit energy waste in the system as a whole.

Despite the possibilities for improved efficiency described above, to which could be added the obvious one (especially in the US) of stimulating the use of smaller, lower performance cars, present trends are towards lower overall efficiency of the transportation system:

> More people buy cars and second cars.
> The average mileage per annum is increasing.
> Increasing traffic congestion causes more waste.
> Increasing polarisation into relatively long-distance high-speed motorway travel and stop–start town driving.
> Car performance is increasing, consequently there is more speeding, fast acceleration, etc.
> High-performance rotary engines are being introduced despite their low efficiency.
> Anti-pollution devices and low-lead gasoline decrease overall efficiency.
> New safety regulations lead to heavier cars.

There seems to be a strong case for looking at these trends towards lower efficiencies and to try to reverse them where possible. Some actions would be: reconsidering anti-pollution and safety regulations, stopping the introduction of rotary engines, setting reasonable limitations to car performance and size.

Domestic/commercial heating and air conditioning

HEATING EQUIPMENT—It has already been argued that extensive penetration of electricity into the domestic heating market is highly undesirable. Gas and oil fired central heating installations are more efficient and should also provide for the other heating requirements in the household through combination with a hot water system. There is even considerable scope for improving the efficiency of such installations. A well designed central heating/boiler installation might have an efficiency between 80 and 90 % as compared to the 70–75 % of present day installations. It is, however, the actual performance in the use that is the important issue and present-day equipment often operates at 50–60 % efficiency partly because of insufficient maintenance, partly because of intermittent use.

TABLE 7
Efficiencies for Residential Energy Uses[a]

| | Efficiency percentage | | | Efficiency ratio |
| | | Electricity[b] | | Gas/ |
	Gas	Utilisation	Overall	Electricity
Space heating	60	100	28	2·1
Cooking	40	80	22	1·8
Water heating	62	91	25	2·5
Clothes drying	50	50	14	3·6

[a] From the report on Conservation of Energy by the Jackson Committee (US Senate), August 1972.
[b] Assuming 28 % overall efficiency in generation, transmission and distribution.

AIR CONDITIONING—Development of more efficient equipment for air conditioning is urgently needed as present day equipment is very inefficient. In this market it is often the low cost of inefficient equipment that attracts customers to use it.

HEAT PUMPS—Heat pumps that extract low grade heat from the ambient air or water can deliver two to three times the quantity of heat required as pumping energy. Therefore the proper use of electric energy, if used for domestic heating at all, other than through storage devices, would then seem to be for driving heat pumps. The overall efficiency of electric heating might then become comparable to that of the direct use of oil and gas. The main disadvantage seems to be the high capital cost of such systems. At the moment the only sophisticated applications are found in some large buildings. There appears to be a good case for a detailed study of this subject to see whether this technology could seriously challenge present objections to the use of electricity for heating purposes. It would be of particular interest to find out what the overall efficiency of a heat pump driven by fossil fuels would be.

INSULATION—Where energy is applied to maintain an enclosure at a temperature different from that of its surroundings the degree of insulation obviously affects the energy requirement. An optimum cost–effective solution can be found dependent on insulation and energy costs. It seems likely that, overall, about half the energy used in temperature regulation could be saved by fully applying available insulation techniques. That such techniques are not more widely applied reflects the present balance between insulation and fuel costs; it can be assumed that increasing fuel costs will favour improved insulation standards. Indications are, however, that savings larger than say 30% are very costly indeed.

As mentioned repeatedly in this report, present trends are not in the right direction. In the US for example there is a significant increase in the average room temperature people desire in winter and a similar decrease in the temperature desired in summer.

Industrial use of energy
Especially in the industrial market the low cost of fuels and electricity has allowed low-efficiency practices to become rather widespread. As was shown in Fig. 2, a no-change extrapolation leads to 50% of all natural gas consumption being in industry. Conversely it is also in this market that increased prices could result in considerably lower consumption. As the industrial market represents some 30 to 40% of the total energy use, the potential for savings would seem to be obvious. The OEP Report estimated US energy savings in this sector that can be achieved through increased energy prices to be some 2½ mbd by 1990.

In the context of this paper it would be impossible to even try to indicate possible savings in the industry as a whole. It is noteworthy, however, that large companies in the US and elsewhere, including General Motors, US Steel and Dupont, have started active energy saving programmes. Refiners, consuming some 5–7% of world oil demand, are fully aware of the importance of such energy savings.

Substitution of materials; recycling of waste materials

A welcome contribution to improved overall efficiency of energy uses would be the replacement of high-energy-content materials by lower-energy-content alternatives. Transportation, packaging and building are areas in which there is large scope for such substitution.

Table 8 shows the approximate energy requirements for the production of various metals, and similar figures for glass, paper and plastics. Multiplication of energy needed per unit weight by the relative weight needed of each material

TABLE 8

Energy Requirement for the Production of Metals, Glass, Paper and Plastics

	ton oil eq/ton[a]
Magnesium	7
Aluminium	4–5
recycle	1
Iron and steel	0·2–0·4
Copper	1–2
recycle	0·2
Zinc	0·5
Glass	0·5–1
Paper	0·2–0·4
Plastics	2 (including 1 for base material)

[a] One ton oil is equivalent to 12 500 kWh (measuring their heat values).

shows, for instance, that in principle the use of aluminium is more energy consuming than the use of iron and, in particular, the use of plastics. Correct comparison is however only possible if one is able to calculate the overall energy content of end products made from different materials. Such calculations are rather difficult as may be illustrated by the fact that even the figures shown in Table 8 are rather tentative. Of course different materials also have different properties, so that any comparison is quite debatable.

In the context of this paper it is therefore perhaps sufficient to draw attention to the importance of possibilities in substitution of materials. One important area where such substitution is expected to take place on a large scale is the substitution of plastics for metals in car manufacture.

Recycle of materials has obvious advantages, as is illustrated in Table 8 for aluminium and copper. A considerable number of studies have been made to investigate the merits of returnable bottles, throw-away bottles, glass recycling against the use of paper and plastics. In this area opinions differ widely and frequently the facts available are not sufficient to come to any firm conclusions. One other example where opinions differ widely is the attitude taken towards the use of plastic bags for garbage collection: in some cities this is forbidden, in others it is compulsory.

Electricity and fuels from waste

In the context of increasing energy efficiency there are obvious advantages in schemes that generate electricity from waste incineration. However, capital costs tend to be relatively high and the total capacity of a municipal waste burning plant is generally only some 20 MW. Furthermore, these plants can only be used for base load power generation. The total electricity production from waste could be of the order of 150 kWh per annum per inhabitant (in Europe), *i.e.* some 10% of the per capita domestic consumption.

Another development is towards the production of gas or oil from agricultural waste and manure by pyrolysis or micro-biological processes. The potential of such schemes is quite large but a more detailed study would be needed to make any comments on the scope of such processes for the near future. In principle the conversion of all US agricultural waste into oil could supply half the current US requirements for oil.

Oil production from agricultural waste is just another way of utilising solar energy. Although it falls outside the scope of the paper the potential of large scale wood production, thereby increasing our use of solar energy, for power generation merits serious attention.

FORCES FOR CHANGE

Having discussed the need for improved efficiency of energy uses and the scope for such improvements it is necessary to give some comments on how changes will materialise, if at all.

From the foregoing it is clear that change is necessary in many areas but that simple measures are not sufficient to cope with this complex problem. Many of the changes suggested by this paper would of course cause side effects that should be considered carefully before any drastic decisions are taken. One also needs to know a great deal more about costs before one can fully appreciate the options available. Clearly worked out solutions have not been given and probably there are quite unique local situations giving different 'right' solutions for various parts of the world.

It seems obvious that there is a role for private enterprise to play; it should view the achievement of economic growth while being confronted with an energy/pollution/resources/capital problem as a big challenge. Also there is an essential role for governments and other authorities to create the right environment for change and where necessary to make choices for the benefit of society where there is conflict of interest.

The authors gratefully acknowledge the assistance provided in the preparation of this paper by all the Shell staff concerned.

REFERENCES

1. R. A. Rice (1970). 'System energy as a factor in considering future transportation', ASME Paper 70-WA/Ener-8.
2. R. A. Rice (1972). 'System energy and future transportation', *Technology Review*, January, p. 31.
3. E. Hirst (1972). *Automotive Engineering*, **80**(7), 36.
4. E. Hirst, 'Energy consumption for transportation in the United States', Oak Ridge National Laboratory, ORNL-NSF-EP-15.

Discussion

Mr R. H. Johnson (Mobil Oil): I think that you describe the position as it is. What you have not done is to describe what might be and what are the implications of the decisions that you have described. This seems to be very confidently based on our present socio-economic system which is capitalist. If we endure that, then it is very hard to see big changes made in the way that we use up our energy, and while there is capitalism we must go on expecting this kind of wastage. We know that General Motors makes more money by selling large cars than it does small cars because a large part of its profits are tied up in spares. It's just the same as we know with the CEGB and other nationalised industries with their sales of electrical heaters. Thus telling the consumer that he's got to be co-operative is not really tackling the trouble at its real source.

Mr H. J. Alkema: Well of course I only mentioned the consumer in the third instance. I said to start with I see this as an enormous challenge to industry. I think this calls for innovation because I don't believe that the first thing should be a suggestion that people should not heat their houses, or not travel, or not do this and that. I think the challenge is to give people the same thing they are used to, which is freedom of movement, freedom of choice, freedom of having a nice big house and heating it, but to help them by giving them the knowledge to do it a little more efficiently, I'm not at all sure that that would not be profitable for industry. If it was not, then that industry we are talking about is the wrong industry. I think we in our industry are coming to this and I don't mean through state control; if industry behaves in this way I think all of us will start behaving thus, I see no problems. I don't believe in state companies.

Mr L. G. Brookes (United Kingdom Atomic Energy Authority): It is an odd fact that points superficially in the direction sought by the authors that in the domestic UK market the consumption of therms per capita—on a heat supplied basis—has actually fallen over the last 20 years. But consumers are abruptly enjoying more value from their therms—better standards of heating and lighting, etc. They are also paying more for today's therms (in the form of electricity and gas) than for yesterday's therms (in the form of coal). Perhaps if energy is presented in an attractive, more convenient but more expensive package we shall move in the direction desired by the forces of the market.

Mr H. J. Alkema: It is of course always difficult to say whether we are moving in this direction. Cases like this are very often expressed in input terms, so what you express here may represent the fact that power generation efficiencies have gone up very significantly, but they don't any more. People close down the efficient power stations to start up inefficient ones because they are cheaper. When you talk about

101

electric heat you could of course, using this argument, say that in 1970 people use less therms than they did in 1920 because you make use of that gimmick of increased efficiency at the power station. It does not detract from the fact that if you used gas instead of electric heating, you would double your efficiency.

Professor P. R. Odell (Erasmus University, Rotterdam): Does not control of energy use imply *energy budgeting* by an authority (governmental or statutory) which examines the energy implications of different ways of doing things (*e.g.* producing electricity, or the transport sector). Otherwise will not institutional interests prevent more efficient use in their own short-term profit earning interests— as, for example, conventional electricity authorities fighting all total energy (on-site generation) systems in industry and commerce by offering specially favourable tariffs to those conformists considering the alternative?

Mr H. J. Alkema: I don't think one should condemn industry and society for the way they have used energy because it has left us with an unparalleled growth of prosperity for the people. We really have achieved something. But, what we must not do is to be too late in finding out that the past way of use could lead to the wrong ending. I think we are at the right moment to correct some trends that could go wrong. What I am saying is that industry is the place where energy investment should be initiated, to create new possibilities, new technologies. Governments will then see that happen and support those they think are right. Industry doesn't need a lot of government intervention (perhaps just tacit approval for most things). Perhaps we'll need support in future things such as fusion and solar energy. I think generally it is up to industry to show people that we can manage these things.

Mr S. E. Churchfield (Burmah Oil): Energy costs provide a connecting link in the four preceding papers. The use of coal will increase as it becomes more competitive as oil prices rise. The ultimately recoverable reserves of oil are dependent upon the price which the consumer is prepared to pay for them. Development of gas reserves in the higher cost, deeper waters of the northern part of the North Sea will depend upon gas prices. Investment in nuclear power stations is related to alternative fuel costs. In summary it seems that energy costs will rise. What, in the authors view, will be the effect of higher costs on consumer attitudes?

Mr H. J. Alkema: In Europe people pay $12–$14 a barrel for oil and they don't know that when they buy electricity for heating they pay $36 a barrel. They don't know, they only spend, say, 10% or 5% of their disposable income on energy, so they don't care.

Mr J. G. Mills (Lindsey Oil Refinery): The speaker has said that the energy gap is being created by the maintenance or improvement in the standard of living. If we use the motor car as a measure of the standard of living then India will require 250 m and China 400 m motor cars to catch-up. Is it possible for other nations, particularly those underdeveloped nations to achieve the American standard of living, or is it a pipedream?

The solution of making energy so expensive that people can't afford to use it would be disastrous, not only for economic growth for it would also create a lot of unemployment.

Mr S. E. Churchfield: So if you are going to eliminate what one likes to consider as the free economy situation, then you are left with only government intervention as a means of achieving the results which are set.

Mr H. J. Alkema: I don't believe in government intervention. I think it should be a gentle adjustment; when our common interest does not move together then of course you need a connection, but I think industry has a reasonable record of showing that it can adjust. This is a much debated point. I could of course take an easy escape and say within the time span we are talking about it won't happen anyway because you have to talk about growth rates and if somebody has $200 per annum today, to get up to $6000 per annum that the Americans have you need centuries.

Mr K. A. D. Inglis: I would like to make one comment. I think the price mechanism is very slow in affecting the efficiency of energy use. I recall that a large number of booklets were produced around 1947 by NIFES, during the period of fuel scarcity immediately after the war; these tended to gather dust until about 1956 when the Suez Crisis threatened a shortage of fuel supplies—there wasn't really a shortage, but a threat of shortage. The booklets were pulled off the shelf, and the lessons put down by NIFES were applied.

The price mechanism never induced this at all, and it hadn't been moving towards more expensive fuel at that time anyway, but the threat of shortage, and a belief in a potential shortage had a very considerable effect on people's attitude towards more efficient fuel use—even though it represented only 12% of their industrial costs.

CHAPTER 7

Modelling Future Energy Supply

M. H. ROTHKOPF

formerly Shell International Petroleum Co. Ltd

H. de VRIES

Koninklijke/Shell-Laboratorium, Amsterdam, The Netherlands

MODELLING FOR THE FUTURE

Forrester and Meadows with the System Dynamics Group at MIT have stimulated computer simulation as a tool for forecasting the behaviour of large socio-economic systems. The following paper describes an application of this type of model building on the world energy supply.

By way of introduction it may be useful to say something about model building in general and our experience with the Club of Rome world models in particular.[1]

MODEL BUILDING IN GENERAL

Model building is increasingly used in the process of scientific investigations as a method to provide answers to specific questions. As such it has certain strong features. It often allows us to draw conclusions more quickly, cheaply and safely than we could if we tried our assumptions out on the real system. Such real-life experiments may even be technically impossible or highly undesirable. A model has the additional advantage that it allows objective discussion of problems and stimulates conceptual thinking. Moreover, experimentation with a model provides a kind of consistency check of the assumptions going into the model, and such experiments will rigorously reveal the consequences of these assumptions.

There is always the danger that relevant aspects are left out of a model. In physics, models are made of the behaviour of existing 'systems' such as pieces of material, electrons, light, etc. Many years of experimentation, together with a long tradition of building physics models, have created a substantial and generally accepted body of theory in this area upon which many models can now be firmly based. But in the social sciences the situation seems to be different.

With any model there is always the question whether it does indeed provide reliable answers to the problem for which it was built; it must therefore be evaluated with regard to its purpose and use.

105

THE CLUB OF ROME WORLD MODELS

The purpose of the 'World' models is to gain insight into the future behaviour of an existing system. The emphasis of the models is very much on the development of 'the global system' through time. In the existing world models this global system is defined in highly aggregate terms, *i.e.* with neglect of internal variety similar phenomena are described collectively by a single number, called a level. Examples of such levels are: Population, Pollution, Natural Resources and Capital Investment. Geographical variations are neglected as each level represents a world-wide average. But also all different kinds of pollution (thermal, radioactive, in air, water or soil) of resources and of investments are lumped together.

The inevitably subjective nature of such models

There is no agreed and generally recognised body of expertise about the global future. Not only do we know little about the present relations that govern global dynamics but we know even less about the mechanisms that will prevail in the future. All factual knowledge must necessarily relate to the past. Therefore any model used for forecasting requires a considerable amount of expert opinion.

In fact it is true to say that any such model is primarily a precise and explicit statement of the model builders perception of our global system and its future. The relevance of the model for the real world depends completely on the expertise upon which it is based, and is hard to assess.

Aggregation and empirical content

Aggregation in itself is not a bad thing and it is the purpose of the model that determines the amount of detail required in it. But if model variables represent a high level of aggregation it may well become more difficult to know the role of these variables in the real system and to interpret its behaviour in terms of them. In other words the model may lose empirical content. This causes interpretational difficulties and makes it very difficult to establish the relationships that should be incorporated in the model.

The Shell analysis of the Club of Rome world models

An analysis of these models was undertaken by Shell International Petroleum Company and Koninklijke/Shell Laboratorium Amsterdam because of the importance of the issues they dealt with and also to study the technique as a planning tool.

In view of the above remarks on model building we can summarise the conclusions from our analyses of the Club of Rome world models fairly briefly. The main conclusion is that these models can generate widely different pictures of the future and therefore do not lead to definite conclusions. As a result they cannot be used to arrive at policy decisions which can be soundly defended.[2]

These results should be seen as signalling a degree of ignorance about future developments which cannot be significantly removed by this type of model.

Human adaptive action plays an important role in determining the future and this should be taken into account when trying to construct any picture of the future.

A unique and true picture of the future can of course never be made. Therefore the essence of planning cannot just be to make forecasts but to make an inventory of those possible developments that are likely to be critical for the future and to shape our organisations in such a way that we will be able to adapt in a timely fashion. Therefore we feel that planning efforts should concentrate on identifying the possible future bottlenecks of today's world and planning the necessary action to overcome them.

In this process modelling is definitely useful. But although world model building may prove to be a useful activity in providing a medium for the confrontation of specialists, it does not seem likely that it will produce a consensus of opinion about issues of a general and highly aggregated nature. With these issues their differences of opinion will just be reflected in the models these people build.

If such a consensus were to be reached about model structure and input data, which is more likely to happen when trying to answer specific questions with special purpose models with a high empirical content, we would still have no certainty about the validity of the model results. But the emerging model would be the very best we had, and it would be foolish to neglect our experts' advice and not use it.

A MODEL OF WORLD ENERGY SUPPLY 1900–2020

We have set out to construct a model that projects total global energy demand into the future and calculates a supply pattern of this demand over a number of sources.

The model
Figure 1 presents a system diagram of the model. The left hand side of the diagram shows the calculation of energy demand. We have assumed that energy demand, with a three year time lag, is proportional to population, proportional to the 0·8 power of material standard of living,* and inversely proportional to the 0·2 power of energy cost.

During the period from 1900 to 1970, 'commercial' energy demand has increased by a factor of about 11 and total energy demand has apparently increased by about half that. Our model shows (*i.e.* is consistent with) an increase by a factor of 5·6.

There are reported studies of attempts to measure the income elasticity of demand for world energy. A recent UN study[3] reported an elasticity of 0·9 for world commercial energy use with world 'GNP' per head for the recent past. This seems roughly consistent with our estimate of 0·8 for all energy.

We are not aware of any good measurements of elasticity of total energy demand with energy cost. This elasticity seems generally to be thought of as low or even as negligible. We have chosen a low but not negligible value because we believe that there are identifiable ways in which higher energy cost will result in consumption reduction, particularly in the long run.

* Defined as per World Model 2—J. W. Forrester (1971). *World Dynamics*, Wright-Allan Press, Cambridge.

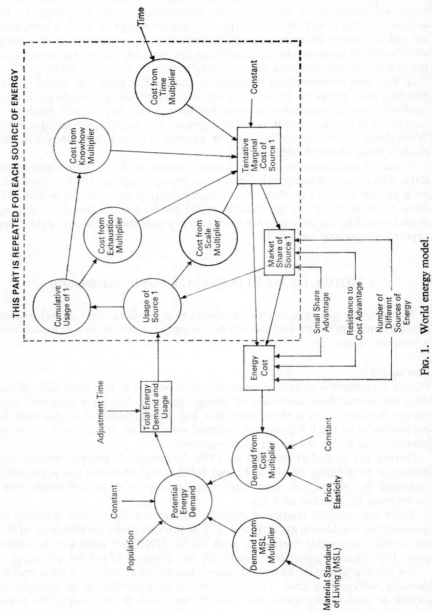

Fig. 1.   World energy model.

The input curves of population and material standard of living versus time have world population increasing from 1·6 billion (10^9) in 1900 to 3·5 billion in 1970 to 5·7 billion in 2020 and material standard of living increasing by a factor of just over 3·5 from 1900 to 1970 and at 3% per year thereafter. These data are slightly low compared with conventional projections.

On the supply side we have assumed that there are four different sources of energy competing for the energy market. These are coal, oil and gas, nuclear, and 'all other' (conventional sources such as hydro-electricity and wood fuel). Nuclear is treated on an input basis and is assumed to exist only from 1970 onwards. The competition between energy sources is assumed to be resolved in terms of relative costs. We have attempted to have these costs reflect the effects of normal technological progress, economies and diseconomies of scale, exhaustion of reserves, and any other effects predictable as a function of time. We have called these costs 'tentative marginal costs' and envisage them as long run marginal costs. We intend them to be expressed in units of constant purchasing power and believe that these relative costs reflect an estimate of relative overall value in use.

In particular, it should be noted that these costs cannot be compared on a dollar per Btu basis. There are many markets where coal, while losing market share, is selling at a cheaper price per Btu than is oil, which is increasing its share.

No attempt has been made to estimate or allow for changes through time in the relative value in use of the different sources. If this model is to be refined, this might well be the place to begin. Such a refinement we think will prove to be a major undertaking involving segmentation of the market by end use and, perhaps, geographically.

Normal technological progress as an agent to change cost

To represent the effects of normal technological progress we have assumed a 'learning curve' type of relationship of the form:

$$\text{cost multiplier} = A. \text{(cumulative production)}^B \text{ with B negative}$$

For coal, oil and gas, and nuclear, we have chosen the exponent such that doubling the cumulative amount of energy produced by the source results in a 15% reduction in unit costs. For the 'all other' category we have assumed that there is no technological progress. The Boston Consulting Group[4] has

TABLE 1

Initial Values of Cumulative Production as at the Initial Year

Source	Initial year	Cumulative production	
		Model units[a]	brl oil equivalent $\times 10^9$
Coal	1900	4·00	134
Oil and gas	1900	0·05	1·67
Nuclear	1970	0·018	0·6

[a] The unit used in the model initially was the amount of commercial energy used in the year 1970—approximately 33·4 $\times 10^9$ brl oil equivalent.

documented this kind of learning curve relationship for a wide variety of chemicals and metals. They do not allow separately for economies of scale as we do in the model. Therefore, in order to be consistent with their historical data, we chose lower coefficients.

The amount of technological progress on a curve of the type we have used depends heavily on the initial value of the cumulative production as at the initial year. Our estimates of these initial values are shown in Table 1.

Economies of scale

In addition there are also possible economies associated with the scale of operation such as efficiencies in logistics and opportunities to spread over-heads over a wider base. For coal and for oil and gas we estimated that doubling of scale of operation would produce a reduction of 10% in costs. For nuclear power we assumed only a 5% cost reduction from doubling, because nuclear power is primarily used to generate electricity and many of the economies of scale of electricity distribution have already been achieved. For all the other categories, we have assumed substantial diseconomies of scale. For hydro-electricity this is due to the diminishing marginal value of dam sites. For wood fuel a large increase in scale would mean intensive tree farming. It was assumed that doubling energy production in this category would increase costs by 60%.

Cost effects as a function of time

Only one direct effect of time on costs was assumed. Early nuclear development has obviously been subsidised by government developed technology and also by private industry attempting to buy into what is expected to be a rapidly growing market. To include the effect we have assumed that, in 1970, when nuclear is introduced into the model, only one third of its cost actually counts and that two thirds is subsidised. The fraction of costs subsidised is reduced gradually (linearly in time) until 1985 when no more subsidy is assumed.

In the nuclear sector we have not included in the time function any allowance for further technological breakthrough (*e.g.* fusion).

Cost increases from exhaustion

Reserves of a resource are normally defined in terms of the amount available at stated costs and with present technology. In order to discuss 'running out of resources', it is necessary to estimate how much of each resource will be available at higher costs and with improved technology. We have already indicated how we estimate the cost effect of technological improvements. Therefore the problem is reduced to estimating the relationship between cost and addition production. Since cheaper sources will normally be used first, it is to be expected that the effect of exhaustion of reserves is to increase costs as the cumulative production increases. The particular functions chosen to represent this effect are shown in Fig. 2. There is little direct quantitative evidence about these functions. Their justification lies in their qualitative correctness, their consistency with what is known about present reserves and discovery rates, and their tendency when used within the model to correctly reproduce historical relative costs and market shares (to the extent that these are known) and to be consistent with our more confidently held predictions. Tar sands and shale oil are assumed included in the exhaustion curve of oil and gas. On the curves in Fig. 2 we have marked the values of cumulative production for the various sources which, under standard run assumptions, are reached by 1972, 1996 and 2020.

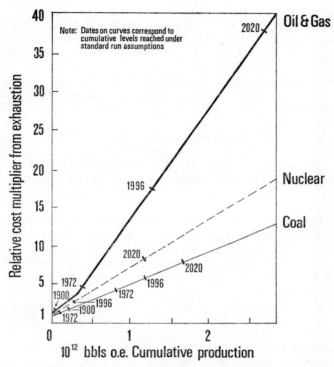

FIG. 2.   Exhaustion curves for oil and gas, nuclear energy and coal.

Market share determination

Market shares for the various energy sources are expressed in terms of their previous market shares and their tentative marginal costs. Along with satisfying the mathematical necessity that market shares sum to unity, this is done with the following properties in mind:

(i) The market share of a source with a low marginal cost grows at the expense of the market shares of those with a higher marginal cost.
(ii) The lower the tentative marginal cost of a source, the faster its market share will grow.
(iii) The larger the market share of a source, the slower the rate of change in its market share.

The model just described is very rough hewn indeed. The effects of depressions and world wars are ignored. Aggregation is at a world-wide level. Even though there are inter-continental fuel shipments and ways of generating electricity from different sources, the concept of a world energy market is a rough one; in the first decades of this century it was still rougher. Furthermore, after some deliberation we have chosen to omit taxation from the model. This has been done, not because the taxes are small—often they dwarf other costs, but rather because taxation is hard to forecast, and is often arranged so as not to cause significant substitution at the margin between competing energy sources.

We have not included any significant new energy source. The higher the costs and the further into the future one projects, the more suspect this omission becomes. Therefore, it would be unwise to use this model to project more than 50 years ahead.

Furthermore the influence that the amount spent on energy may have on the development of GNP is left out. If a systematic increase in energy cost caused GNP growth to slow down this would result in a higher percentage of GNP spent on energy.

Note also that we have restricted our attention to the costs of supplying energy. These costs must include the costs of controlling pollution associated with the production of energy. They are not intended, however, to include the costs of controlling pollution associated with the consumption of energy.

Results

The 'results' that are presented here are the output of the model under the assumptions described in the previous section. This output covers the period from 1900 to 2020. The results with respect to periods after 1972 should be thought of as assumptions about the future that are consistent with the assumptions of the model and the input, and not as scientifically or logically compelling conclusions.

The model gives results that are basically in accord with the world's energy history from 1900 to 1970 (to the extent that we know it). While this is an indispensable property for such a model to have, it is no scientific validation. It is possible that quite different sets of parameter values would also reproduce the basic energy history.

Figures 3 and 4 contain the basic results of the model. Figure 3 presents the market shares of each energy source and the total energy demand. Figure 4 shows corresponding costs for each source and for energy overall.

These pictures show coal taking over more than half the energy from fuel wood and other non-commercial energy early in this century and then yielding to oil as the leading source of energy. Oil, in turn, yields to nuclear energy early in the next century. Declining energy sources do not disappear completely. In particular, coal is a significant source of energy throughout. Only its share and not its absolute level declines. Oil peaks in market share in the 1980s although its absolute level continues to increase into the next century.

The cost of oil decreases during the first half of this century and then increases at a relatively rapid rate. The cost for coal is level at first and then increases gradually. The cost for nuclear is low throughout, although increasing after the year 2000. At first this low value is caused by the assumed subsidy. Overall energy cost declines during the first half of this century and rises thereafter. The increase during the next 48 years averages out at under 1·5% per year. The increase in the cost of oil and gas during this period

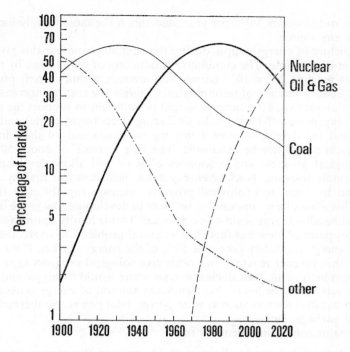

FIG. 3. Standard run—market shares.

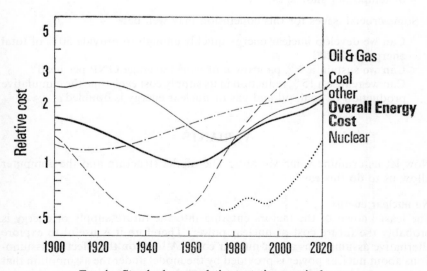

FIG. 4. Standard run—relative tentative marginal costs.

averages out at under 3·0% per year, and this is the most rapidly increasing cost for any source.

The picture of energy supply during the next 50 years that this gives does not seem implausible. The cumulative production of oil and gas by the year 2020 has reached $2·7 \times 10^{12}$ barrels—an amount within current projection of what exists.[3] In spite of technological progress the cost has increased by a factor of about five. This increase should be sufficient to support the production of expensive offshore crude (including deep ocean crude) and Arctic crude, and the development of a thriving tar sands and oil shale industry. Coal reserves will not be exhausted. The cost increase of about 50% plus technological progress and economies of scale will allow development of more remote reserves. Nuclear energy costs, held down at first by subsidy and then by rapid technological progress, increase rapidly after the year 2000. This allows large amounts to be spent in developing low grade uranium ores and handling large scale waste disposal. This is hardly optimistic from a resources point of view but there are technical problems to overcome before nuclear energy can safely take over 50% of the energy market. If we were to assume that breeder reactors and other technological progress kept nuclear costs from increasing, then nuclear market share would be bigger and overall energy costs would be lower. No significant amount of energy is assumed to come from novel sources such as solar power, tidal power, geothermal steam, recycled garbage, etc.

The major conclusion seems to be:

> If global GNP per head grows at 3% pa then the percentage of GNP spent on sources of energy would rise from 3% now to 4% by 2020. This growth of expenditure does not look like a critical development and from it one may conclude that there will be no global shortage of energy before 2020. This, however, certainly does not rule out the possibility of local or temporary shortages.

Some crucial issues for this conclusion may well be:

> Can we develop nuclear energy quickly enough to provide 50% of total energy by 2020?
> Can we sustain a 3% pa growth of world average GNP per head?
> Can we realise a 15% reduction in its supply cost each time the cumulative production of coal, oil and gas or nuclear energy is doubled?

VARIANTS

Now let us examine some variants. The model structure and the computer allow us to do this easily.

No nuclear energy
The least known of the factors entering into the future supply of energy is probably the future cost of nuclear power. Therefore it is useful to explore alternative assumptions about nuclear costs. A limit on the effect of assumptions about nuclear power is provided by the model under the assumption that nuclear power never becomes economic. The results of this assumption are

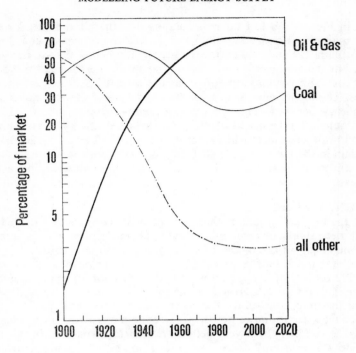

FIG. 5.   No nuclear energy—market shares.

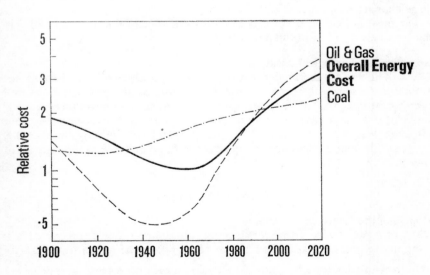

FIG. 6.   No nuclear energy—relative tentative marginal costs.

shown in Figs. 5 and 6. Under this assumption the oil and gas share of the energy market peaks around 1990 and gradually declines as coal begins to expand again. Oil and coal costs are only slightly higher than in the standard model, but the absence of low cost nuclear power has driven up the overall energy costs substantially. Energy costs increase at 2·8% per year from 1968 to 2020. The higher energy cost has had some small effect in holding down total energy demand. The 'all other' category supplies about 75% more energy but still remains under 4% of the total energy. The cumulative production of oil and gas has reached $3·2 \times 10^{12}$ barrels by 2020—18·5% more than in the base case. By 2020 cumulative coal production has reached almost $1·9 \times 10^{12}$ barrels of oil equivalent; it too has increased by just under 20% versus the base case.

Fixed GNP per head

One of the original questions that prompted the construction of this model was the desirability of economic growth. Therefore it would be interesting to see the effect on the model of eliminating economic growth. The energy model so far has been run using a 3% per year per head economic growth after 1972 on top of a population growth projection of approximately 1% per year. This results in a growth in energy demand of $(1 + 0·8 \times 3) = 3·4\%$ per year before correction for the effect of energy cost changes.*

Under the assumption of no per head economic growth, energy demand is assumed to rise at 1% per year before price effect correction. In this context the model shows overall energy cost increasing at 0·8% per year from 1972 to 2020 versus a base case increase of just under 1·5% per year. In 2020 oil and gas costs are 18% below the base case value and coal costs are actually 5% higher. Largely owing to the allowance for exhaustion of uranium reserves in the standard case, nuclear costs may stay noticeably lower than standard run values during the last two decades simulated. There are no large changes in market share.

The most noticeable effect is coal's fall from 14% of the market in 2020 in the base case to $9\frac{1}{2}\%$ in this no-growth case.

No normal technological progress

While the effect on the model of stopping economic growth per head is not dramatic, the effect of stopping normal technological progress is that overall energy cost increases at 2·7% per year during the next 48 years (versus 1·5% per year in the base case). During this period, oil and gas costs increase about 3·9% per year, nuclear costs by 3·7% per year, and coal costs by almost 1·0% per year. The major effect on market shares is to favour coal at the expense of nuclear.

CONCLUSIONS

Modelling the future energy supply

What have we gained from constructing our market share forecasts *via* a computerised model? As agreed before, the input to the model is necessarily

* This correction, a reduction of 0·2% per year for each per cent per year of energy cost increase, is always small.

largely subjective and therefore the results cannot lead to indisputable conclusions. This is no different from 'conventional' forecasts and in comparison there are some advantages.

In the model's construction we have made explicit our economic and technological assumptions. The energy supply picture coming out of the model is rigorously consistent with these assumptions. The model allows us to determine what energy supply picture for past and future is consistent, within the models structure, with each set of assumptions about its input variables.

Cost reduction from technological progress, economies and diseconomies of scale, cost increases from exhaustion and projections of world-population and GNP growth are in an explicit and quantitative way taken into account.

Any 'conventional' forecast of energy market shares will also have to consider the above or similar factors. But the extent to which assumptions need to be made explicit and the way in which assumptions lead to conclusions is rather obscure for the conventional forecasts, which we may want to think of as resulting from 'mental models'.

So what we gain from mathematical modelling is largely explicitness of model structure and rigorous consistency of assumptions and conclusions within this structure. But the distinction between good and poor forecasts lies in the future.

ACKNOWLEDGEMENT

We are grateful for the contributions of our colleagues in Group Planning and Research. In particular we thank Ir. M. M. J. Tellings of the Koninklijke/ Shell-Laboratorium, Amsterdam, who has programmed the model.

REFERENCES

1. D. L. Meadows et al. (1972). Limits to Growth, Earth Island Ltd.
2. T. W. Oerlemans, M. M. J. Tellings and H. de Vries (1972). 'World dynamics: social feedback may give hope for the future', Nature, 238, 251.
3. Resources and Transportation Division, Department of Economic and Social Affairs, United Nations (1971). 'World energy requirements and resources in the year 2000'. Paper at the 4th UN International Conference on the Peaceful Uses of Atomic Energy, Geneva, September.
4. The Boston Consulting Group (1968). Perspectives on Experience.

Discussion

Professor D. C. Leslie (Queen Mary College, London): Figure 2 of the paper shows the cost of nuclear energy as increasing seven-fold between 1972 and 2020, due to resource exhaustion. If the number refers to the total cost of nuclear energy after correction for the inflation of general cost levels, then I regard an increase of this magnitude as inconceivable. The purchase of uranium ore accounts for 10% of the cost of energy from thermal reactors, and much less than this from fast reactors, and a tenfold increase in uranium prices would only double the cost of nuclear energy.

This relative immunity to raw material costs is not the least of the attractions of nuclear energy.

Dr H. de Vries: We are getting into the interpretational problems here. This sort of model is more specific than the Club of Rome world models. If you want to see a markedly changed role for nuclear energy you have got to show that it is competitive. So these costs reflect an overall value of energy to the network and include all costs and not just fuel costs. As in the case of local power stations it is the capital cost that is the main thing, so capital costs come into the overall value of the energy we use.

Mr M. B. Bolt (National Coal Board): On what basis did you assume 50% of energy would be nuclear by the end of the century, because this implies (for the UK for example):

   (i) *Building* some 7500 mW of nuclear stations a year—about three times the average actually achieved for any station over the past decade.
  (ii) *Economics* of all nuclear electricity systems are attractive, also that load following problems are solved for nuclear stations.
 (iii) *Investment* constraints are not applicable when the above assumptions would require a said £5 m/day for the next 27 years.

Dr H. de Vries: This question shows there is no consensus of opinion about the future of energy. An important task for this model building activity is that it helps specialists in the different forms of energy to consult with each other and find out where the real bottlenecks are.

Mr L. G. Brookes (United Kingdom Atomic Energy Authority): May I comment on the point made by the Coal Board representative that nuclear plant could not be introduced in the quantities suggested because of logistic and capital constraints.

Over the last 50 years electricity consumption in the UK has increased by a factor of 50. The prediction for the UK by CEGB is for a factor of 4 by 2000 AD—really very modest. If the capital resources for this plant are not to be found from the

GNP then it implies that we shall not maintain even the present relatively low rate of GNP growth, for electricity growth at this rate is wholly consistent with GNP and total energy growth rates of 3 to 4%.

Professor A. Williams (University of Leeds): One important constraining influence on the growth of particular energy producing sections is environmental pollution. Is it possible to include this factor in the model?

Dr H. de Vries: We wanted to include the cost of overcoming pollution, not just associated with supplying the energy but with also with the use of the energy, which is where the major pollution is. We believe this is going to have a great bearing on the overall volume of energy use. However, we did not do so in the end because of the difficulty of making appropriate estimations of these costs.

Miss M. P. Doyle (Esso Petroleum Co. Ltd): Is the 0·2 elasticity for energy price and demand consistent with the no technological progress case which showed a very rapid progress acceleration of prices? How does this affect the proportion of GNP going to energy supply?

Dr H. de Vries: There is no feed-back in this model between the amount of money spent on energy and GNP growth. In fact the GNP growth is an autonomous input. If the costs grow considerably quicker than your total GNP, this is going to have a down-grading effect on GNP growth.

Professor P. R. Odell (Erasmus University, Rotterdam):
    (i) Is the 27% pa increase in unit costs of energy based on a zero-inflation assumption?
   (ii) How is the long-run marginal cost of oil established? What assumptions lie behind the oil and gas exhaustion cost curve?

Dr H. de Vries: It is with zero inflation since you never know what inflation it is going to be; you assume income and costs are subject to the same conditions.
    As I have said to Professor Leslie, it is very difficult to tear apart the cost influences from exhaustion, technological know-how and scale. One recent paper suggests there is a 20% cost reduction every time your cumulative production doubles, and that would be the effect of technological progress. This does not separately account for economies of scale, so we have taken a little bit lower figure and said: every time cumulative production doubles cost is going to be decreased, because of technological progress, by 15%. The justification of the resulting line lies in that it reproduces the picture that people who are knowledgeable in the energy field recognise. There is also direct evidence of course, because we can see that cumulative production figures in terms of present day reserves, and whether the time when you reach exhaustion does seem realistic. For all these sorts of models it is difficult enough to say what the percentage of the total world demand will be supplied by various fuels. It is far more difficult to talk about exhaustion. However, everybody says exhaustion is an important factor, so we try to put it into the model as best we can. We are happy to discuss it, but are not pretentious about this line.

Mr K. A. D. Inglis (British Petroleum Co. Ltd): You mentioned that you were giving us a highly aggregated model. In fact how homogeneous is the world you are dealing with, and are problems, such as the balance of payments and the reaction of the third world that does not have oil and gas and which faces considerable escalation in the cost of energy. Is it assumed in fact that you go with the rest of the world, or is it going in the reverse direction?

Dr H. de Vries: If you want to do something sensible in forecasting or planning you ought to identify where the bottlenecks are. These do not seem to be in the global balance of supply and demand; and that is what this model is about. In modelling these socio-economic systems, we have not really been able to come to any conclusions about social factors, like what the relations between the third world and the developed world will be, and I do not think you will find an answer in this type of model.

CHAPTER 8

Nuclear Energy 2: From Fission to Fusion

D. C. LESLIE

*Professor of Nuclear Engineering, Queen Mary College,
University of London, UK*

A MILD DISCLAIMER

The title seems to imply that we will go 'from fission to fusion'. Since I don't regard this progression as inevitable, I should perhaps say that the title was chosen by the Institute of Petroleum. Fission is, of course, with us now; fusion is, in the unkind words of a Guardian letter-writer, waiting to be invented. I will be speculating later on the chances of success.

WHY DOES THE FAST REACTOR NEED TO BE FAST?

If the question had been 'Why do we need the fast reactor?' the answer would have been obvious from Chapter 5 (for those of you who didn't know it before). An enriched thermal reactor can extract only 2% of the energy potentially contained in uranium; a fast reactor can extract 25 times as much energy from the same quantity of uranium. Thus the fast reactor will certainly be needed in the long term, if we fail to develop a satisfactory fusion reactor.

If I had asked, 'What is a fast reactor?', I think that most readers of Chapter 5 would have answered confidently (and correctly) that it was one in which the mean neutron speed was high.* However, I would guess that most people outside my own industry are hazy about why a fast reactor uses uranium so much more effectively than a thermal reactor. I shall explain this point, since it is crucial to an understanding of the special difficulties of the fast reactor.

When a fissile nucleus splits, the bulk of the energy goes into the fission fragments; it is then degraded into heat as these fragments collide with the crystal lattice of the fuel. The fission also produces a small number of neutrons. The average neutron yield depends on the nature of the fissile nucleus and on the energy of the neutron causing the fission, it varies between 2·5 and 3·1.

---

* The mean neutron speed in a thermal reactor is typically about 5 km/sec; in a fast reactor it is roughly 1000 times higher.

One of these neutrons must go on to cause a further fission, if the chain reaction is to be sustained. The remainder may leak out of the reactor core, be absorbed unproductively, or be absorbed in fertile material. The first two facts represent a waste of neutrons. Leakage can be reduced by making the core large. Absorption can be controlled to some extent by using materials with low absorption cross-sections. However, some absorption in fission products and in control rods is inevitable; also, some neutrons are absorbed in fissile nuclei without causing fission.

The fertile nuclei are U-238 and Th-232. Natural uranium contains 99·7% of U-238, while natural thorium consists entirely of Th-232. Therefore our nuclear energy resources are overwhelmingly in the form of fertile material. The rare but fissile U-235 (0·7% of natural uranium) is the key which unlocks this treasure, since the absorption of one neutron converts a fertile nucleus into a fissile nucleus. If we can arrange for at least one of the neutrons coming from each fission to be absorbed in fertile material, then the reactor will just replace the fissile material it is consuming. If it can do better than this, and can make more, it is 'breeding' and can in principle release the entire energy content of uranium or thorium.

Examination of the nuclear data shows that good neutron economy can be achieved either with very fast neutrons or with very slow ones, but not with neutrons of intermediate speed. This accounts for the very sharp distinction between fast and thermal reactors. The data also show that it is not possible for a thermal reactor fuelled with uranium to breed. A thermal reactor fuelled with thorium can just breed, but it is a rather skin-of-the-teeth operation which will not become economic until uranium and thorium prices have risen far above their present levels. Fast reactors breed quite easily, and this is chiefly because unproductive absorptions are much lower than in thermal reactors. Quite high breeding ratios* can be achieved in plutonium-fuelled fast reactors, since the fast fission of plutonium produces more than three neutrons.

THE DESIGN PHILOSOPHY OF FAST REACTORS

To illustrate the differences in design concept between thermal and fast reactors, I shall describe the changes which would have to be made to convert an AGR into a Gas-cooled Breeder Reactor (GBR). We start from AGR because gas is the only coolant which is seriously proposed for use in both thermal and fast reactors.

As most of you will know, the core of an AGR consists of a large block of graphite with several hundred vertical cylindrical holes in it. These are the coolant channels, and they contain the fuel, which consists of UO_2 rods canned in stainless steel. The outer diameter of the cans is about 14·5 mm. Our first step in converting this arrangement into a fast reactor is to remove

---

* The efficiency of fuel utilisation is determined mainly by the ratio of the number of fresh fissile nuclei formed to the number of nuclei undergoing fission. This is called the Breeding Ratio or the Conversion Ratio according to whether it is greater or less than 1.

the graphite moderator, whose sole purpose is to slow the neutrons down. This would leave large gaps between the fuel clusters, which must then be brought closer together to leave an appropriate flow area for the coolant. The resultant void round the edge of the core could be eliminated by repositioning the boilers and contracting the pressure vessel.

When we come to restart the reactor after making these alterations, we shall find that it won't go critical; by removing the moderator, we have pushed the neutron spectrum into the intermediate region where absorptions are very high. The only remedy is to increase the concentration of the fissile material, and we shall use a mixture of plutonium and natural uranium in preference to enriched uranium because in fast reactors the fission yield of Pu-239 is higher than that of U-235. The reactor will go critical again when the Pu concentration has reached about 10% (of all heavy metal atoms). With a Pu concentration of 12% the neutron economics have become very favourable, and breeding ratios as high as 1·4 are possible.

At first sight it seems that this evolution has produced a very attractive reactor. Its capital cost will be lower than that of AGR since, by removing the moderator, we have reduced the size of the pressure vessel. In addition it can release 50% or more of the energy potentially contained in uranium ore, while AGR can release only 2%.

Unhappily, two factors cloud this apparently favourable picture, since the changes which converted an AGR into a GCFR (Gas-Cooled Fast Reactor)* have impaired both safety and fuel economics. The moderator of AGR represents a substantial heat sink, which delays the overheating consequent on a loss or reduction of coolant flow, and this heat sink is apparently not available in the GCFR. (In fact, there may be ways of restoring it without affecting reactor performance.) Also, in AGR any rearrangement of the fuel can only turn the nuclear reaction off. This is not true in GCFR, and it is possible (or, at least, not demonstrably impossible) for melt-down of the core to produce a small nuclear explosion. This is the Bethe-Tait accident, a safety problem unique to fast reactors.

I don't want to make too much of these safety differences, since I think it could be demonstrated that our hypothetical GCFR shares the crucial safety feature of AGR: this is that there seems to be no credible way in which fuel melt-out can actually occur. The real and crippling drawback of our new reactor is that it is uneconomic. Its core contains about five times as much fissile material as that of the AGR from which it was derived. Remembering that fissile material costs (ore purchase plus enrichment) account for about 20% of the cost of power from an AGR, and allowing for the fact that the GCFR is breeding while the AGR is consuming fissile material, we find that GCFR electricity is 50% more expensive than that from AGR. Too much has been made of small differences in costs, but this difference isn't small.

Another difficulty of our AGR-derived GCFR is that its doubling time† is over 90 years. Many people have argued that doubling times must be got down below 10 years, which is a typical timescale for the doubling of electricity

* This is an alternative name for the GBR.

† The doubling time of a fast breeder reactor is the time which it takes to make enough plutonium to fuel a second, identical reactor.

demand. I regard this argument as misconceived, since it ignores both the contribution of thermal reactors and the slowing-down in the rate of increase of electricity demand which must occur sooner or later. However, unless we manage to develop fusion fairly quickly, we shall need breeders whose doubling time is much less than 90 years.

The remedy for both difficulties is to increase the fuel rating. The European Association for Gas Breeder Reactor* has produced a design of this kind, with a fuel rating of about 85 MW/tonne; the general arrangement of this design, which is known as GBR 1, is shown in Fig. 1.

The fuel rating of the later AGRs is 12·5 MW/tonne, and the higher rating of the GBR 1 design is obtained by using smaller pins and higher gas

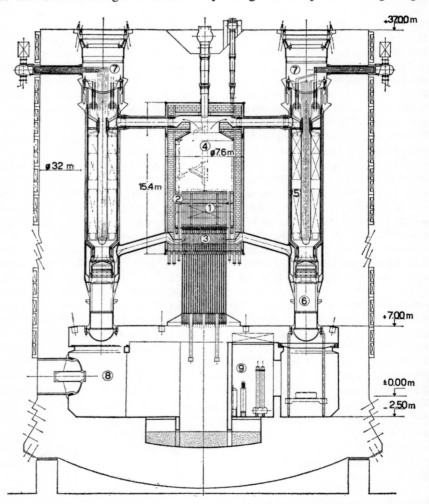

Fig. 1. General arrangement of GBR 1 (by permission of GBR Association, Brussels).

* Short title: GBR Association.

pressures.* Though many technical problems remain, I think that the feasibility of this design is not in doubt. It is the safety which remains to be analysed and demonstrated. We noted that there are minor safety difficulties with a GCFR, even when the fuel rating is no higher than that of AGR. These difficulties naturally become much more severe when the fuel rating is increased by a factor of nearly 10. The rating of the GBR 1 design is chosen to minimise the power cost. In my view, we should be prepared to reduce the rating, perhaps even to halve it, if this would make the safety arguments appreciably easier.

THE SODIUM-COOLED FAST REACTOR†

We have used the GCFR or GBR to illustrate the special problems of the fast reactor, but at the moment this is not the preferred line of development. All countries with active fast reactor programmes are concentrating on the LMFBR because of the vast fuel ratings which are possible with sodium cooling. The other great advantage of this coolant is that it gives adequate heat transfer performance at atmospheric pressure. Therefore it is quite feasible to design a reactor in which an accident initiated by loss of coolant is impossible.

Naturally enough, sodium has its disadvantages. It burns in air and reacts violently with water. Since the steam cycle seems to be the only way of converting the thermal energy of hot sodium into electricity, the chemical reactivity of sodium necessarily implies that the LMFBR is going to be a difficult and expensive reactor. In particular, the sodium-to-water heat exchanger shows every sign of being a difficult piece of equipment.

A less obvious disadvantage of sodium is its adverse effect on the neutron economy. Even when the coolant passages are made as small as possible, the minimum plutonium enrichment for satisfactory performance is around 20%, and this gives a breeding ratio of about 1·2 (the corresponding figures for the GBR are 12% and 1·4). The high enrichment implies that the rating of the LMFBR will have to be extremely high, if the power cost and the doubling time are to be reasonably low. The heat transfer properties of sodium are so good that this is perfectly possible, and in this respect the design has a pleasing self-consistency. The mean fuel rating of the Prototype Fast Reactor (PFR) at Dounreay is 160 MW/tonne, and 600 MW of heat are produced in a core 0·9 m high and 1·45 m in diameter. Figure 2 shows the layout of the PFR primary circuit.

Because the rating is so high, there must be no interruption of the coolant flow. However, the coolant passages are so narrow (to improve the neutron economy) that it is not easy to demonstrate that they cannot be blocked. This is the main safety issue of the LMFBR.

* The GBR Association has also produced other designs, with more sophisticated fuel elements.

† This type is often referred to in the literature as the LMFBR = Liquid Metal (Cooled) Fast Breeder Reactor.

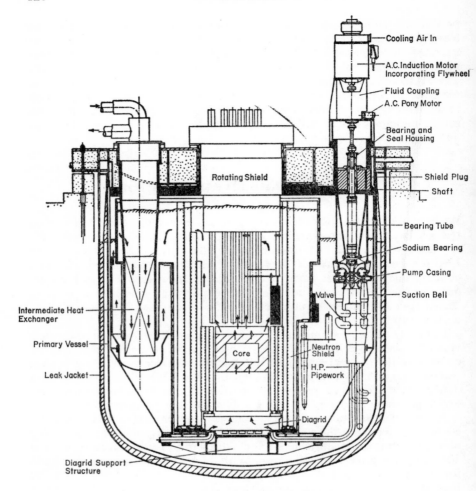

Cooling Air In
A.C. Induction Motor Incorporating Flywheel
Fluid Coupling
A.C. Pony Motor
Bearing and Seal Housing
Shield Plug
Shaft
Bearing Tube
Sodium Bearing
Pump Casing
Suction Bell
Valve
Neutron Shield
H.P. Pipework
Diagrid
Rotating Shield
Intermediate Heat Exchanger
Primary Vessel
Leak Jacket
Core
Diagrid Support Structure

FIG. 2.   The PFR primary circuit.

FAST REACTOR PROSPECTS

There is a strong school of thought which holds that the fast reactor must be introduced as quickly as possible. The reason usually given is that we shall run short of uranium if we stick to thermal reactors, though it is sometimes argued that a developed LMFBR would be cheaper than a developed thermal reactor.

I don't think either argument is correct. As I said in Chapter 5 there should be enough uranium to meet mankind's needs with thermal reactors until well into the 21st century, though it will only be available if we go and find it. Also, I do not believe that LMFBR is really competitive with thermal reactors at today's uranium prices (if uranium is expensive enough, the fast reactor must be cheaper than any thermal reactor).

It would be equally wrong to go to the other extreme and to conclude that the fast reactor is unnecessary. I assume that humanity will always need some form of nuclear energy; this implies that, if we do not succeed in developing an economic fusion reactor, we shall need the fast reactor sooner or later. The sixty-four dollar question is when we shall need it, and the answer will be determined by the evolution of electricity demand, by the rate at which new uranium deposits are found, and by progress with fusion. I think the best guess that anyone can make now is that large-scale installation of fast reactors will have to start not later than the early years of the next century.* This gives us 30 to 40 years in which to sort out the technology of fast reactors, and this should be sufficient. A substantial effort must be maintained on the LMFBR, and I should like to see much more work done on the GBR. This type may prove to be essentially cheaper than the sodium-cooled fast reactor, and much of the technology is now quite familiar.

THE FUNDAMENTALS OF FUSION

Fission energy is obtained by breaking up the heaviest nuclei, while fusion energy comes from the amalgamation of the very lightest nuclei. Fission is induced by neutral particles which can move freely through matter, and the fissile nuclei do not have to move. Fusion occurs when two fusile nuclei bang together sufficiently hard to overcome the electric repulsion between them. Fusion reactions only occur at a useful rate when the fusile material is heated to temperatures in excess of 100 million °C.

At a fixed temperature, the fastest thermonuclear reaction is that between deuterium and tritium (the D-T reaction). The reaction rate between deuterium nuclei (the D-D reaction) is about a hundred times slower, and all other reactions occur so slowly that it is hard to imagine that they will ever be exploited commercially (these other reactions are important in the evolution of the stars).

Heavy water (deuterium oxide) is present in all natural water at a concentration of about 200 ppm, and the oceans are therefore an almost inexhaustible source of fusion energy. Their total energy content is over $10^{10} Q$, and this energy can be 'mined' without desecrating the landscape. Indeed, the total fusion of the deuterium in one gallon of water produces more heat than is obtained from the (chemical) burning of 300 gallons of petrol. However the D-D reaction is comparatively slow, and it is certain that the D-T reaction will be exploited first. Tritium does not occur in nature; it is made by the neutron bombardment of lithium,† and we need to assure ourselves that this element is available in quantities sufficient to justify a large R and D programme.

Lithium is very little used at present, and there has been no serious attempt to look for lithium deposits. Even its average crustal abundance is uncertain by a factor of as much as five. Natural lithium is at least four times as abundant

* W. B. Lewis (AECL-4445) points out that this decision can be postponed for at least 50 years by using CANDU reactors.

† Since the D-T reaction produces a neutron, the process can be made to sustain itself.

as uranium, but less than one-thirteenth of it can be burnt in a fusion reactor.* There is certainly more than 10^6 Q of lithium in the rocks, and there is every reason to think that we shall find substantial high-grade deposits when we start to look for them. The sea also contains more than 10^6 Q of lithium, but this may be difficult to extract because it is chemically similar to sodium.

The immediate attraction of fusion is not that it is expected to be much cheaper than fission, or that deuterium is so abundant; this is irrelevant while we are limited to the D-T reaction. It is on environmental grounds that fusion scores so heavily. The total radioactivity is minute compared to that in a fission reactor; there are no risks of explosion or of loss of coolant, and there are no potentially dangerous materials for ill-disposed people to steal. These advantages would be sufficient to make us opt unhesitatingly for fusion if it was as well developed as, and no dearer than, fission. Indeed, they are great enough to justify a substantial extra cost.

Therefore, if a commercially acceptable fusion reactor can be developed by (say) 2010, it seems quite possible that the fast reactor will never have a large share of the market. However, I don't think it likely that the timescale for the development of the fusion reactor will be as short as this. The first fission reaction was achieved in December 1942. Now, thirty years later, the simpler thermal reactors have just about been brought to commercial maturity. So far as fusion is concerned, 1942 hasn't dawned; we have yet to achieve a self-sustained fusion reaction. Also, it is already clear that fusion technology is more difficult than fission technology.

The present wise policy of many governments is to step up their effort in fusion research, without assuming that this work will bear fruit in time to help them out of the difficulties with which they are now struggling. Fission chain reactions are by their very nature self-sustaining, but this is not necessarily true of fusion reactions. Fusile material must be heated before the fusion reaction can start, and it is only too possible for the requisite heat input to exceed the energy produced by the reaction. This is, in fact, the position we have now reached. We have produced thermonuclear reactions, but their yield is small compared with the heat required first to warm the material up and then to counterbalance radiation losses.

Lawson[1] has worked out the minimum condition for a fusion reaction to be self-sustaining. For the D-T reaction at a temperature of 2×10^8 °C in a practical reactor, the product of the particle density n and the reaction time τ must be greater than 1.7×10^{14} cm^{-3} s. For the D-D reaction, the optimum temperature is three times higher, and the minimum acceptable value of $n\tau$ increases to 6.3×10^{15} cm^{-3} s. These numbers show clearly that the D-T reaction will be very much easier to exploit.

FUSION BY MAGNETIC CONFINEMENT

The Lawson criterion shows that the fundamental problem of fusion technology is to hold the reacting medium together for long enough to recover

---

* T is produced by the neutron bombardment of Li-6, which forms 7·4% of natural Li. The energy content of a tonne of Li-6 is not very different from that of a tonne of U.

the energy invested in heating it up. The temperatures are so high that material walls are useless, but the high temperature also implies that the medium is completely ionised and that it can in theory be contained by a magnetic field. In practice, it turns out that all the obvious configurations are violently unstable, and that confinement times are too small by factors of 10^6.

This difficulty has been the overriding theme of fusion research for the past 15 years, and it seems that it has now been resolved. The Tokamak machine in Moscow gives confinement times of about 0·1 s and particle densities of the order of 10^{13} cm^{-3}. To satisfy the Lawson criterion, both

1   Plasma (15m Radius)
2   High Vacuum
3   Cell Structure (20m First Wall Radius)
4   Lithium
5   Graphite
6   Lithium Header
7   Thermal Insulation
8   Support Structure (Stainless Steel)
9   Iron
10 Borated Water
11 Lead Cladding
12 Cryogenic Envelope
13 Typical Blanket Coolant Pipes
14 Typical Shield Coolant Pipes
15 Containment Lining
16 Biological Containment
Restraints for :-
17 Magnet-Shield & Blanket Weight (Compressive)
18 Magnet Reaction Forces (Compressive)
19 Magnet Weight (Tensile)

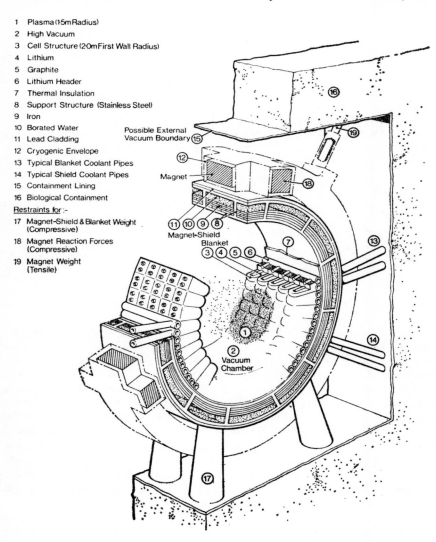

FIG. 3. (a)

numbers must be increased 10 times, and on present evidence this can be done by building a bigger machine of the same type. Unless there are yet more difficulties waiting for us round this last corner, the self-sustained fusion reaction should be achieved by 1980. Fusion will then enter a technological phase, in which the main task will be the development of a commercial reactor which is more or less competitive with the fast fission reactor. Figure 3 shows a Culham design study for a power-producing fusion reactor based on the Tokamak principle of containment.

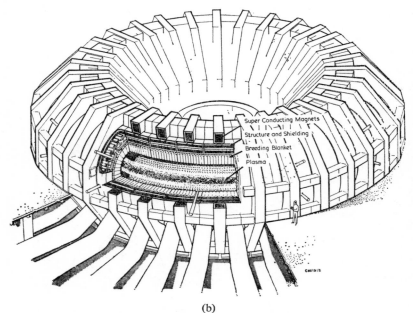

(b)

FIG. 3.   Design study for a Tokamak-type fusion reactor.

For two reasons, both of which are connected with the need to use super-conducting magnets,* I am not too optimistic about the chances of success in this second phase of the work. The reacting medium or plasma will be at a temperature of hundreds of millions of degrees. The magnet will be less than 2 metres from the plasma, and yet its temperature must be kept down to 4 K. The magnet must also be shielded almost perfectly from the intense gamma radiation coming out of the plasma. These considerations make the technology of magnetic confinement seem rather hostile. Moreover, studies at Culham show that if the magnetically confined fusion reactor is to compete with the fast fission reactor the present cost of superconducting magnets must be cut by a factor of something like 10. There certainly will be some cost reduction (in real terms) but personally I find it hard to believe that they will be as big as this.

* A fusion reactor contained by a conventional magnet would inevitably consume more energy than it produced.

FUSION BY ABLATIVE COMPRESSION

Magnetic reactors attempt to satisfy the Lawson criterion by containing very dilute plasmas for long times. If matter of normal density $n \simeq 10^{22} \, cm^{-3}$ could be heated to thermonuclear temperatures, the Lawson criterion would be satisfied by containment times of less than a microsecond. The only plausible method of producing such heating is to focus a spherically symmetric laser pulse onto a spherical pellet of fusile material. Inertia would hold the pellet together for the necessary containment time, with some help from the pressure of the laser light. Theoretical studies suggest that the method is feasible, with some reservations about how much light might be absorbed by the pellet. However, a net gain of energy can only be achieved if the energy in the heating pulse is more than 10^8 joules. We do not know, indeed we cannot even imagine, any way of producing pulses of this size.

Happily, deeper study shows that nature is for once working with us. The immediate result of focussing an intense spherical light pulse onto a spherical pellet will be to evaporate or ablate material from the surface of the pellet. This process implodes the remaining material by a mechanism similar to that which propels a rocket, increasing its density by a factor of more than 1000 and thereby reducing the minimum pulse size for energy gain to a few tens of kilojoules. This is not much more than is available now, and we can confidently expect to be producing pulses of this size within a few years. The laser pulse length should be about 25 nanoseconds, and at the end of the compression the fusion energy will be released in a few picoseconds (10^{-12} s). The pellet will then be blown apart, the explosion being the equivalent of 5 to 50 lb of TNT (these figures are taken from the pioneer paper of Nuckolls et al.[2]).

On present knowledge, which is admittedly very inadequate, this method looks attractive and a number of groups are attempting to put together the apparatus for a preliminary test. It is conceivable, though not likely, that the first self-sustained fusion reaction will be achieved with ablative compression and not with magnetic confinement.

THE PROSPECTS FOR FUSION

The potential market for fusion is very large, and the crucial question is whether it can be made reasonably competitive with fast fission. I see no reason to doubt either that a self-sustained reaction can be achieved by magnetic confinement or that this system is capable of producing electricity. It seems likely that this electricity will be expensive, though this gloomy view could easily be overturned as development progresses. Ablative compression looks more natural, but its attractions may diminish as we come to understand the problems better. I am sure that the proper strategy is to maintain a very substantial effort on both methods, at least to the point where one of them begins to look clearly preferable.

SUMMARY

a. The resources of both fissile and fusile material are adequate to meet humanity's energy needs for an indefinite time.
b. Fusion is safer than fission, and it also produces fewer environmental problems. However it is not available now and it is not possible to say when it will be. For the present, we must rely on fission.
c. Unless we succeed in putting fusion on a commercial basis in a few tens of years we must switch to fast fission reactors, but there is no need to make the change immediately.
d. Fast (fission) reactors are in some ways more difficult than thermal reactors, and it would be prudent to introduce them slowly.
e. Gas cooling may be an attractive alternative to sodium cooling for fast reactors, and development effort on the GBR should be increased.

REFERENCES

1. J. D. Lawson (1957). *Proc. Phys. Soc.*, **70**, 6.
2. Nuckolls *et al.* (1972). *Nature*, **239**, 139.

Discussion

Mr K. A. D. Inglis (British Petroleum Co. Ltd): Where is fusion research going on—is it as worldwide as fission research and development, or is it much more concentrated?

Professor D. C. Leslie: It is worldwide. All technologically advanced countries are in this. The Russians have been consistently the leaders in magnetic confinement. It is their faith and vision which has brought it to the verge of technical feasibility. Japan has a large programme, so have we. Their current establishment is a large one—ours has been run down of late. Euratom is mounting a substantial effort. It is international, and it is less at the moment subject to commercial security wraps than is fission technology.

Mr P. R. Cooke (Powell Duffryn Ltd): Can you explain how temperatures of $100 10^6$ °C can be generated and what materials of construction, if any, can be subjected to these very extreme temperatures.

Professor D. C. Leslie: You can cope with it in two ways—this is what the two methods of confinement are about. In magnetic confinement, the material is fully ionised—those temperatures strip all the planetary electrons away from the nuclei. You then have charged particles, though the plasma as a whole is neutral. But it is made up of charged particles which if a magnetic field is applied, instead of travelling in straight lines go riding round the lines of magnetic force. So by applying sufficient magnetic field you can constrain the particles to gyrate round the lines of force so that they never approach the material wall.

There are a number of methods of heating. It can be done by just putting in a direct current. You can do it by accelerating the particles in an accelerator and then putting them almost one by one into the plasma. It is a very contentious subject how it should be done.

The other method of confinement of course is not to confine them at all—this is what is done in the ablative compression method. You have this little pellet and until the laser light shines on it it is cold. It reaches these enormous temperatures very rapidly, blows itself apart; it will be in a large chamber, ten feet across, and by the time the material has reached the walls of the chamber, it is no longer hot.

Mr P. R. Cooke: Of what then do you construct the chamber? What materials are you looking for?

Professor D. C. Leslie: Well, again it depends on which methods you are using. I can be much clearer about magnetic confinement because much more work has been done on that. The reactor will almost certainly be in the form of a torus.

The figure shows a conceptual design of a Tokamak-type magnetic confinement fusion reactor. It is in the shape of a torus. The conditions on the first wall are very challenging; there is a big heat flux and a very high flux of both neutrons and gamma rays, all coming from the plasma. But it looks as though materials can stand it. Indeed conditions on that wall are comparable to those of the fuel can of a fast fission reactor.

Mr G. Chandler (President, Institute of Petroleum): How is this effort going to be undertaken? Will it be successful through the normal process of competitive or co-operative research, or will it require a Manhattan or Apollo type project to bring it to fruition?

Professor D. C. Leslie: I think all the evidence is that the methods that have brought the thermal fission reactor to usability will do for this one too. That is why I think the time scale is long. I don't greatly believe in Manhattan type projects for this sort of thing—I think reliability and engineering sense come with time.

Mr G. Chandler: Though fission started with the Manhattan project and was a great boost to it, of course cost was quite unimportant. And cost has been unimportant in the Apollo activity. Does fusion need a Manhattan project as a point of departure?

Professor D. C. Leslie: No, I don't think so. I don't know how we would spend really large amounts of money now—I think we would tend to lose contact with economic realities. You might possibly be prepared to pay 50% more for a fusion reactor than a fission reactor, so if fusion is ten times as expensive, it will never come in. People aren't going to pay that sort of cost differential. They might pay 50% more for the environmental advantages. Once costs come in, Manhattan is wrong— what is wanted is people beavering away chipping cents off here, but all the time remembering safety, reliability and price, putting the three together.

Mr R. H. Johnson (Mobil Oil): As a matter of safety, by the time you've reached whatever year you feel that fusion reactors may be commercial, let's say 2030, either by that time we would have had a disaster of some kind with a fission reactor or we would not. On the basis that we have not had one, do you think we would be prepared to pay the other 50% more for the apparent extra safety provided by a fusion reactor rather than fission reactors?

Professor D. C. Leslie: One can only give a subjective answer here—there is of course something between a disaster and no disaster, that is an incident which is disquieting but is recognised not to be a disaster. My guess is that we will have one of those in the next 60 years. There probably won't be a disaster, but maybe we'll release a 1000 curies somewhere, maybe some hundreds of people will have to be evacuated for a few days and it will slow fission up for a while.

I think the basic argument is that the longer you operate fission reactors the greater the chance of some disaster occurring becomes. And I personally would be prepared to pay 50% more; other people might be prepared to pay more than that, others might not be prepared to pay any premium at all.

Mr J. M. C. Bishop (Phillips Petroleum Co. Ltd): In your papers all references to the use of atomic power have been based on the conventional use of generated heat. What are the development prospects for direct use of particle energy?

Professor D. C. Leslie: Very little, for this reason. The deuterium/tritium reaction looks very much easier. When we try to design reactors for deuterium/deuterium the numbers come out rather frightening. If you wanted to do it by ablative compression then you would be back with the 10^8 joules per laser pulse. The deuterium/tritium reaction produces only neutrons so there can be no question of direct harnessing of charged particles, you've got to use the nuclear plus kinetic energy of the neutrons. If we ever get deuterium/deuterium, and I very much hope we will, then something like two thirds of the energy is in the form of charged particles and expansion against a magnetic field to produce electrical energy directly is conceivable. There are some schemes that look quite interesting, but not even for the 21st century.

Mr S. E. Churchfield (Burmah Oil): Your paper emphasises the potential safety/environmental advantage of the fusion process. Do you consider first, that it will be realistic to install fusion reactors in inhabited areas, *e.g.* in the Battersea Power Station; and secondly, that it will be possible to construct small power units using the fusion process suitable for installation in ships or even motor cars?

Professor D. C. Leslie: I don't think we really understand the safety of these beasts. This work is mainly being done at Culham. A group there called the Fusion Technology Study Group are doing design studies on the assumption that Tokamak will work in the larger sizes. They do safety studies as a part of engineering feasibility, but to do safety studies on a thing you don't really know how to design is very difficult. The only substantial risk seems to be the release of the tritium inventory which is about one kilogram. Now the body is very tolerant to tritium but there is an upper limit to the dose. I think one wouldn't choose to put it at Battersea Power station until one has a certain amount of experience. My guess is yes that would be feasible and all the studies show that it's not on in sizes less than a few giga watts, by either method. Now that may come down as we get to understand it better, but it does look like a central electricity generator and nothing else, whereas the high-temperature reactor is a possible source of process heat for steel making, beneficiation of coal, and so on. I don't see the fusion reactor in that category at the moment, but this may be just because we don't know enough about it.

Mr E. W. Lang (British Petroleum Co. Ltd): Uranium must be processed before it can be used in nuclear reactors. In general it has to be enriched for use in thermal reactors and converted to plutonium for use in fast reactors. Enriched uranium and plutonium production capacities are therefore probable limiting factors in the development of thermal and fast reactors. Would Professor Leslie comment on the availability of these nuclear fuels?

Professor D. C. Leslie: This may have been the real bottleneck in the installation of nuclear power. The great bulk of enriching capacity in the world as a whole is in the hands of the USAEC. They've been not ungenerous in the past though the terms they've announced recently are very very stiff, but the point Mr Lang made to me in private conversation is that it is probable the Americans are going to want all that capacity before the end of this decade. What does the rest of the world do? The answer is that it has got to get cracking on building its own separation capacity. Europe is well on with centrifuge technology and all the assessments show that this is cheaper than diffusion. But we can't delay the decision to build very much longer. If we do we are going to find ourselves in difficulty over our materials.

The only alternative is to build CANDU and that is why I gave some emphasis to it yesterday. CANDU uses natural uranium and needs no diffusion plant or centrifuge. It is intermediate in uranium utilisation between the enriched thermal reactors and fast reactors. It can burn about five per cent, maybe even ten per cent of the total wealth represented by a uranium deposit.

So even if the prospectors don't have the success I expect, and sea water extraction proves difficult, CANDU could take us well on into the next century. It remains an option if we do run into serious trouble. I have tried to do sums about fast reactors, but I find it quite impossible to know what fissile material supplies will be available for them. But it would be possible to start them on uranium 235. Fast reactors will work on uranium 235, but there is a type of diminishing spiral because you don't get a good breeding growth. So there is an argument for a shorter doubling time and therefore the generation of more plutonium, though I am unhappy to see that put before absolute safety.

Mr K. A. D. Inglis: I imagine that you can't have anything comparable with dual firing—once you've designed for U-235 presumably you can't move to another fuel?

Professor D. C. Leslie: I think you could—in fact there are experiments going on in one of the American boiling water reactors which was originally designed to use U-235 but now has plutonium in it. However, I don't think this line will be pursued because plutonium should be kept for fast reactors as long as there is 235 available. What one might even be able to do is to switch over to thorium—thorium gives you much better economy in thermal reactors, but it is worse in fast reactors. The picture is so complicated and the uncertainties so great that I find it difficult to know whether we will be in a bind for fast reactor fuel at the end of the century. It is very likely that we will be in trouble in the early eighties for fuel for thermal reactors. I don't think we need be but we've got to take a decision very soon.

Mr C. L. Goodacre (Consultant): (a) Is the so called 'hydrogen bomb' a clean fusion bomb process? (b) Was Einstein right in thinking the next war would be fought with bows and arrows?

Professor D. C. Leslie: My answer to the first question is no, it isn't. It has a fission trigger, but people worry a lot about the fallout from bombs. The fission trigger for a multi-megation hydrogen bomb is no bigger than an ordinary fission bomb, so compared to the yield the fallout is low. It is theoretically possible to ignite a hydrogen bomb by the use of laser compression and that's where the work I was talking about—ablative compression—started. I'm not much sold on the idea of clean bombs—by the time one begins to use them it matters little if they are clean or dirty, and also even the cleanest of bombs is going to induce a great deal of radio-activity in the earth, which I think will greatly outweigh the fission fallout; so I'm not much bothered whether they are clean or dirty. But I am very interested that the ablative compression reaction is clean, that there are no fission products, and that there is just a small amount of induced radio-activity.

I should say Einstein was right on the second question and the general feeling is that he has at least kept us free of major wars. It's 30 years now since the last one, which is a very long time as far as world history goes.

Professor P. R. Odell (Erasmus University, Rotterdam): I think as an outsider one must contrast the pessimism of the oil and conventional energy industries we have heard expressed this morning and yesterday with your overriding optimism in terms of the development of nuclear and eventually fusion power. This is staggering to someone who is outside both industries and trying to make economic sense out of the whole situation. One wonders if the conventional wisdom about conventional energies is wrong, if in fact we should take your line instead and say, if we go out and look for something we'll find it; if we go out and look for lithium we'll find it. If we were able to say the same about oil, and our predictions about 300 000 million tons were proved wrong by a factor of two or three, then we would be in a situation in which with that kind of expenditure of money on conventional energy, we might be able to do without the fission stage, the dirty stage if you like, in the development of nuclear power. We could then go on to your cleaner stuff in the second quarter of the 21st century. This contrast in attitude and outlook at this stage is staggering—one is also staggered by the fact that the oil industry now has so little faith in its own ability to do its job, that it has to go along and support the dirty stage in the development of nuclear power.

Professor D. C. Leslie: Let's take those two backwards. I must say again, fusion hasn't been invented. And it really isn't safe to stake the future of humanity on something we haven't got. We are absolutely right to work on it, to be prepared to introduce it at the earliest possible moment, but to count on it at this moment in time would be foolish.

On resources, the oil industry has put a great deal of effort into prospecting and as we heard yesterday the estimates all converge on about the same answers. The reason why we're so much more optimistic than the oil industry is that our energy is much more concentrated. We do know roughly how much there is because we know crustal abundance. The only question is where it is. And in the case of fast reactors we can burn the rocks. I reckon the fast reactor can well afford to pay a few pounds a gram for uranium. By comparison with large-scale gold and copper mining operations I think uranium could be extracted from 4 parts per million granite (of which there is untold abundance) at that sort of price. I think our optimism is well justified—I assume that the oil industry has thought very hard before being pessimistic and that their pessimism is also justified!

CHAPTER 9

New Sources of Oil—Oil Sands, Shales and Synthetics

M. W. CLEGG

British Petroleum Co. Ltd, London, UK

INTRODUCTION

The rapid growth in the world's demand for oil, coupled with the finite resources from which such demands can be met, has featured prominently in the active public debate on the world's energy position which has developed over the past few years. The increasing costs of exploration and production development associated with conventional oil have led to greater consideration being given to the large, known, non-conventional sources of oil—oil (or tar) sands, oil shales and coal. Research and development effort on methods for recovering and processing oil from these resources has grown significantly over the past decade, and a commercial-scale plant is already in operation in one of the major tar-sand areas. More will undoubtedly be commissioned in the next decade. This paper looks at the location and magnitude of these resources, the technical and logistical problems associated with their exploitation, and attempts to assess the contributions they could make to the world oil and energy pictures over the remainder of this century.

THE RESOURCES

The existence of substantial deposits of tar sands and oil shales in various parts of the world has been known for many years, but economic and technical problems have precluded their development on any scale. Coal, of course, has been known and exploited for centuries for use as a primary energy source but it is only recently that the possibilities for manufacturing synthetic liquid fuels and natural gas have been considered. In order to get some feel for the magnitude of the resources under consideration it is worth looking at the currently accepted figures for in-place reserves (Table 1).

Converting the coal to barrels of oil-equivalent on a thermal basis means that the total known deposits in-place are equivalent to $43\,000 \times 10^9$ brl oil, and although recovery factors cannot realistically be determined at this time, even a very low figure of 10% would give a recoverable reserve of

141

$4 \cdot 3 \times 10^{12}$ brl oil-equivalent—which is some seven times as large as the currently proven recoverable oil reserves, and significantly larger than the figures projected by experts for the ultimate reserves of crude oil in the world. The following paragraphs on the individual resources give some specific details.

TABLE 1

Oil Reserves in Non-Conventional Sources

	10^9 barrels	10^9 tons
Tar sands	1 487	
Oil shales	6 850	
Hard coal		6 860
Brown coal and lignites		2 100

Heavy oil and tar sands

A distinction between heavy oil reservoirs and tar sands (or oil sands as they are now called in Canada) is frequently drawn, although the physical characteristics of the two oil accumulations may be similar. In general, both types of reservoir cannot be produced by conventional methods and the crudes they contain usually have API gravities less than 15° and contain relatively large amounts of sulphur. 'Tar sands' is the term formerly associated with the Athabasca deposits in Canada, and hence with the concept of recovery by mining techniques whereas 'heavy oil' reserves are usually located at somewhat greater depths below the surface and therefore require some form of *in-situ* recovery technique to be applied. The major accumulations of heavy oil and tar sands in the world are given in Table 2.

TABLE 2

Heavy Oil and Tar Sands

Country	Area (acres)	Overburden thickness (ft)	Volume in-place (10^9 barrels)
Canada	8 000 000	0–2 600	780
Venezuela	6 000 000	0–3 000	700
USA	75 000	0–2 000	2
Malagasy Republic	96 000	0–100	2
Others			3
			Total = 1 487

The main points to notice about these reserves are, firstly, that almost all of them are located in the Western Hemisphere (equally divided between North and South America) and, secondly, that the in-place volumes in both Canada and Venezuela are comparable with the currently estimated recoverable conventional crude oil reserves of the world. Various estimates have been made of the recoverable reserves from these areas but it is extremely difficult to hazard a guess until techniques have been developed further for the exploitation of these resources. However, it seems reasonable to say that:

(i) Some 10% of the Athabasca tar sands may be recoverable by means of surface mining, from which 70–80% of the crude can be extracted.

(ii) The recovery of oil by *in-situ* techniques from deeper deposits of tar sands and heavy oil are unlikely to be greater than that from conventional oil reservoirs, and probably substantially lower.

Oil shales

The reserves of oil associated with oil shales are fundamentally different in character from other oil reserves in that the oil is not present as a liquid but is contained within the shale in the form of kerogen. Crude oil can only be recovered from the shale by the application of heat, the kerogen decomposing at a temperature of about 370°C, to yield a relatively light 'shale oil'. The world-wide deposits of oil shale are very extensive and although estimates have been made of the in-place reserves of oil they are still subject to considerable uncertainty. The current view of the major reserves in the world shows the major reserves in the USA and Russia, with substantial accumulations also in China and Brazil. Once again, the Western Hemisphere contains a significant proportion of the estimated reserves and, as in the case of tar sands and heavy oils, it is difficult to translate the in-place volumes into recoverable reserves. In some ways it is perhaps even harder since the quality of the oil shale deposits (the volume of oil per ton of rock) can vary from as low as 10 to 100 gallons per ton or more.

Coal

Coal reserves are much more widespread around the world than any of the other non-conventional sources of oil. Reserves are normally split between hard coals, and soft coals and lignites. The major areas and their reserves are listed in Tables 3 and 4.

TABLE 3
World Hard Coal Reserves

Country	Reserves in 10^9 tons		Total
	Measured	Inferred	
USSR	145	4 076	4 221
USA	72	1 028	1 100
China	75	936	1 011
UK	127	28	155
India	13	93	106
South Africa	37	35	72
Canada	43	18	61
Others			134
			6 860

From these tables it will be seen that the USA, Canada, South Africa, Australia, India and the USSR all have substantial reserves, mainly at depths of less than 1200 metres. The recovery of coal depends on the use of mining techniques and the estimation of recoverable reserves will be very closely linked to the economics, which in turn will be strongly dependent on

TABLE 4

World Brown Coal and Lignite Reserves

| Country | Reserves in 10^9 tons | | Total |
	Measured	Inferred	
USSR	105	1 301	1 406
USA	9	397	406
Australia	49	47	96
West Germany	62	—	62
Others			130
			2 100

depth, thickness of seam, and location. However, there are substantial reserves of near surface deposits of coal in the USA, Canada, Australia, for example, from which the recovery will be high.

THE TECHNOLOGY OF EXPLOITATION

Exploitation of non-conventional sources of oil falls naturally into two main areas—production and processing. Consider first the production phase. The basic difference between conventional and non-conventional sources of petroleum is that the latter cannot be made to flow by purely mechanical methods at more than a minimal rate—in the case of the solid sources, of course, this is zero. In order to extract the oil from its natural environment one must therefore adopt one or other of the following methods:

(i) Add substantial quantities of heat to the formation, so that, for example, the viscosity of the tar oil is significantly reduced and the oil can be pumped out of the formation as a 'conventional' crude oil, or, in the case of oil shales, the kerogen is converted into shale oil which will then flow to production wells;

(ii) Use diluents or emulsifiers for removing the oil from the heavy oil bearing formation or from the tar sands;

(iii) Mine the source-rock, and extract or process the material on surface.

There are a number of ways of injecting heat into the oil bearing formation, e.g. the injection of hot water or steam, the injection of air to support a combustion front. Although these have been successfully operated in some oil reservoirs, from a commercial point of view the injection of high pressure steam has been the most successful method, and substantial volumes of oil are currently produced in both the USA and Venezuela by this means. All fluid injection methods demand that the source-rock should have a reasonable permeability so that the large quantities of fluid required can be injected into the formation. Unfortunately, many of the sources considered do not have this property, *e.g.* oil shales, coal and some tar sands. Research has been carried out to investigate the feasibility of artificially creating permeable channels within the host rock either by hydraulically fracturing the formation, or, on a much larger scale, by detonating explosive charges (nuclear, perhaps) in the formation. Such methods are still in the early stages of development and their ultimate feasibility is highly speculative.

In the Athabasca tar sands field experiments have shown that crude oil can be extracted but the recovery operation and economics are far from viable at the present time. The feasibility of using diluents for recovering the viscous crudes present in heavy oil and tar sands has been considered but the large viscosity contrast between the diluent and the oil causes rapid fingering of the diluent, a very low recovery of oil from the formation, and hence an uneconomical process.

The recovery of oil shales, tar sands and coal by mining is basically a more straightforward and simple process to evaluate than *in-situ* methods. The techniques of mining and surface handling are well known from other industries. Two possible methods must be considered:

(i) Open-cast—in which the overburden is stripped and the carbonaceous material removed.
(ii) Underground methods—such as room and pillar or lateral access.

Clearly the economics of these methods will depend on the depth at which the resource is located, the thickness of the pay zone and, in the case of open-cast mining, the relative thickness of the overburden and pay zones. In addition there are now significant environmental problems to be overcome in open-cast operations, particularly in the USA.

It is worth drawing attention to the scale of mining operations involved in providing the feed for a plant producing, say, 100 000 bd of crude from the Athabasca tar sands. Approximately 200 000 cu yards of tar sands per day would be required and perhaps two or three times this volume of material would have to be stripped and ultimately replaced after the tar sand had been removed and the area restored. By any standards this would be a very large mining operation.

Turning now to the processing requirements, there are basically two problems:

(i) *The extraction* of the hydrocarbons from the mined oil sand or shale;
(ii) *The conversion* of the extracted crude oil or coal into a transportable and marketable product.

The extraction of oil from the oil sands requires a physical separation process based on the use of hot water, steam and diluent additions to break the oil/sand bonds. Such a process is in use at the Great Canadian Oil Sands plant in the Athabasca tar sands. The oil shales, on the other hand require heating to 370°C or more in order to convert the kerogen (a chemical bonding of the oil to the shale) into a conventional liquid oil. The heat transfer problem in oil shale retorting is relatively large because of the quantities of heat that have to be transferred from hot gases and/or solids. At the present time the techniques of retorting oil shale are still under development and large scale pilot plants are being constructed in the western USA to evaluate these techniques.

The 'crude oils' produced from both the oil sands and the oil shales require further processing or upgrading to make them into acceptable refinery feedstocks. The oil sands crude is a heavy, very viscous, high sulphur crude which must be hydrocracked, or coked and hydrogenated, to yield a lighter, low viscosity crude suitable for transporting and refining. There are obvious disadvantages in locating upgrading plant in the remote tar sand and oil shale areas and research is being carried out into the possibility of pipelining such very heavy crude either as emulsions or as segregated fluids with oil flowing inside an annular ring of water (a process which has been field tested in Indonesia). If such pr ocesses are technically feasible it may be possible to locate the upgrading facilities at traditional refining centres.

The oil recovered from the shale retorts is similar to conventional crudes in some respects but has a very high nitrogen content (which must be removed to prevent poisoning of catalysts used in refining processes), a high viscosity and a high pour point. Processing would involve distillation, coking of the residue and/or hydrogenation.

The production of synthetic liquid fuels from coal requires the development of new technologies for hydrogenation and the manufacture of hydrogen from coal or coal-derived material. The processes require efficient catalysts to work at the high temperatures and pressures necessary in the hydrogenation phase. The oil yields per ton of coal vary substantially with the process—H-coal, for example, is estimated to yield 3·6 brl oil/ton coal whereas the COED (Char Oil Energy Development) process yields only 1·4 brl/ton. In the latter case by-product values are very important in the process economics.

THE CURRENT POSITION

The major efforts currently being directed towards the development of non-conventional oil sources may be classified under three basic headings—commercial projects, existing and planned; large-scale pilot plant projects; and research projects. Only one operation can be described as a commercial-scale project today—the Great Canadian Oil Sands (GCOS) plant in the Athabasca tar sands. The plant, which came on stream in 1968, now produces about 45 000–50 000 bd of 38° API synthetic crude using a surface mining/hot water separation/coking-upgrading process. Start-up problems were severe both in the mining operation, where the diggers on the bucket wheel excavators found difficulty in coping with the very abrasive tar-sand material, and in the processing area. These appear to have been overcome now, and capacity is likely to be increased to 65 000 bd in the next few years, subject to government approval.

One other large-scale project is planned for the Athabasca tar sands—a 125 000 bd plant for Syncrude Canada Limited. This is scheduled to come on stream in 1976/7 and will use a mining/hot water separation technique with upgrading by the H-oil process. The mining operation will involve the use of giant draglines rather than the bucket wheels of GCOS, and dumper-trucks rather than moving belts for the transportation of the oil sand to the processing area.

The only other large-scale project planned is a Brazilian one in the Irati oil shales. Here a plant to process initially 2200 tons/day of shale to yield about 1000 bd of synthetic crude based on the Brazilian state oil company's process (Petrosix), with the intention of ultimately expanding the plant to produce 58 000 bd of oil.

Various other commercial-scale projects have been proposed and discussed over the past few years—for example a Shell proposal for a 100 000 bd plant in the Athabasca tar sands using an *in-situ* steam injection process—but at the present time these cannot be considered likely to come on stream within the next five years.

Large-scale pilot plants

Moving on to the second level of effort—the large-scale pilot plants—there are a number of these existing or planned in North America. Doubtless further impetus will be given to this particular scale of development activity by the recent Presidential statement on energy which sought to encourage US companies in the energy business to find new ways to exploit the very large indigenous (potential) reserves of energy in the USA. In the oil shales of the Colorado/Utah area Colony Development Corporation recently completed a three year experimental programme on a 1000 tons/day plant using the Tosco II process. Another large-scale project is being planned by SOHIO to apply lime-kiln technology to the retorting of oil shales. In addition, the debate continues on the technical feasibility and environmental acceptability of using nuclear explosives in the shales to provide large fracture systems within them, to be followed by *in-situ* retorting.

The Office of Coal Research (OCR) in the USA is providing support for a number of pilot plant projects on coal-liquefaction—amongst them the 'Solvent Refined Coal (SRC)' process which is being evaluated by Pittsburg and Midway Coal Mining Company on behalf of OCR in a 30 tons/day plant. This process involves the dissolution of coal in oil manufactured by the process, and catalytic hydrotreatment of the solution. The main products are about 20% light oil and 80% of a very high viscosity product—which could be described as either a low sulphur (0·8%) refined coal, or a low sulphur very heavy fuel oil.

The H-coal process, developed by Hydrocarbon Research Inc., also involves the hydrogenation of the coal and is currently operating on a pilot plant of 5–10 tons/day. This is a development of the H-oil process for upgrading heavy, residual oils to lighter, low sulphur oil using the ebullating bed technique. The possibility of adapting the H-coal process to the production of gasolines (from Australian coal) rather than low sulphur fuel oil has also been studied.

The alternative to direct hydrogenation of coal—pyrolysis—is being developed in a 36 tons/day COED plant in the USA. This yields much smaller quantities of synthetic oil than the hydrogenation routes but large quantities of high sulphur 'char'. The technical problems of using this 'char' commercially remain to be solved.

Other projects on a pilot plant scale are being, or have been, carried out in the Athabasca tar sands, to investigate the feasibility of *in-situ* recovery techniques. The results so far have not been too encouraging.

Research projects
At the research level it is not possible to detail individual projects, but the types of problem under investigation include the continued evaluation of the many ideas that have been put forward for the liquefaction of coal; the retorting of shale in the ground; the nature of the Athabasca tar sands deposits and the adaptation of secondary recovery techniques to the production of Athabascan oil; the development of new catalysts and techniques for hydrogenation of heavy oils and the removal of sulphur.

Apart from the problems discussed in this section, which might be called broadly the technological aspects of developing non-conventional sources of oil, there are other equally important logistic and environmental ones to be considered. Most of the processes being developed require large quantities of water, but the resources are located generally in areas with rather limited water supplies (the tar sands of Canada are probably the major exception). The resources, almost without exception, are located in areas remote from those where the energy is consumed. The utilisation of large quantities of raw material presents major environmental problems—for example open-cast strip mining of coal and the disposal of spent shale. These problems can hardly be solved in the same way as technical ones for they depend to a great degree on the precise location of the operation. However, the magnitude of the problem is likely to be impressive if non-conventional sources are developed in significant volumes over the next decade. Two million barrels per day of synthetic oil might require between 200 and 700 million tons of raw material feed each year!

DISCUSSION

Two points emerge rather clearly from the previous sections of this paper. Firstly, the world's resources of coal, oil shale and oil sands represent an energy source that is orders of magnitude larger than existing conventional crude oil reserves; even when compared with current world energy demand and future projections, these resources are still very large. Secondly, the technology for exploiting these resources for the production of liquid hydrocarbons is, with the exception of some areas of the Athabasca tar sands, still at the research/development/pilot plant stage. Much development work remains to be done to provide the pilot plant data necessary to design adequately a full-scale commercial plant.

It may possibly appear odd that, in talking about these resources, no mention has so far been made of costs and economics. This oversight was deliberate, for apart from the surface mining developments in Athabasca there is nothing more than paper studies to assess the economics of the various processes currently being looked at. A number of general comments can be made, however, to summarise the rather speculative figures that are published from time to time. The capital investment involved in the mining, processing and upgrading facilities will be not less than $400 million and could be as high as $500–600 million for a 100 000 bd plant, at current costs. Taking account of operating costs, depreciation charges, transportation to consumer areas, on-going research, etc. plus a reasonable return on capital investment it seems likely that synthetic crude values would have to be at least $5 to $7 per barrel in the USA, and even higher in those consumer areas such as Western Europe and Japan which have greater transportation costs from the external sources of supply.

Although the detailed economic studies must still remain uncertain until the technology has been developed further it is possible to make some broad generalisations. The liquefaction of coal is likely to remain the most expensive of the processes considered in this paper and although demonstration plants may be built in the USA over the next decade it seems unlikely that it will be developed on any scale there whilst other, less expensive, alternatives exist— unless these latter fail for technological reasons. Outside North America some development of coal liquefaction on a limited scale in countries where coal reserves exist (but no other indigenous alternatives) may occur, but this probably depends on the technology being developed in the USA. The National Petroleum Council (NPC) in their 1971 report on the US Energy Outlook suggested that 5–8 years plus an expenditure of $50–80 million would be needed before the construction of the first commercial-scale plant. Their 'conservative' assessment of available capacity in 1985 of 80 000 bd seems reasonable; an accelerated development to 850 000 bd by 1985 does not.

At the present time the costs of producing oil shales seem likely to be less than those for liquefying most types of coal. In addition, the technology is better understood and less severe. In the USA, however, the limited supplies of water in the oil shale areas cast some doubt on the feasibility of developing the reserves to their full potential, but there seems no doubt that the levels projected by the National Petroleum Council of 100 000 to 400 000 bd in the USA by 1985 are attainable.

The Athabasca tar sands present the best prospects for development over the next decade, firstly because a plant is in existence and has been producing for several years and secondly because the technology of the exploitation of surface-minable deposits is quite well understood. The technical problems are far less severe than those associated with oil shale or coal liquefaction. Again, referring to the NPC report, a level of production ranging from 500 000 to 1 250 000 bd is deemed realistic by 1985 and figures of 3·5 mbd by the end of the century have been forecast. Such a level could well be approaching the limit of production potential in the surface-mined area of Athabasca.

For coal and oil shale it is difficult to estimate how developments will grow post-1985 since much will depend on other factors such as conventional crude oil reserves, environmental problems, coal conversion technology. What can be said, however, is that unless positive steps are taken now to expand the research and development effort on coal conversion and oil shale processing then the production levels projected for the USA in 1985 may not be met. The considerable lead times involved in developing new processes, testing them in pilot plants and designing and building commercial plants are such that it is the efforts now being devoted to them that will determine their contribution to the 1985 energy pattern. In addition the demand levels for these resources in the future may be closely related to the developments in nuclear energy particularly in the post-1985 period.

In conclusion two major points emerge from the topics discussed in this paper. Firstly, the potential reserves of oil associated with the known resources of coal, oil shale and oil sands are enormous; their contribution to the future demands for oil, however, depend on the solution of the many outstanding technical, environmental and logistic problems. Secondly, there is a need to recognise now the likely requirements of the next two decades, in order to ensure that the necessary research and development work is completed in time. It must be appreciated, however, that investment in this type of long lead-time research and development effort is unlikely to meet the normal investment criteria of commercial companies. Their investments will obviously be restricted, and in some cases will duplicate work by others. To increase the scale of investment and rationalise the research and development programmes clearly requires some governmental or even inter-governmental co-operation and funding.

Discussion

Mr R. G. Whorrod (Imperial Continental Gas Association): Will the author please comment on the energy balance resulting from tar sand oil production, bearing in mind that not only heat but also large amounts of water are needed.

Mr M. W. Clegg: I believe that as far as the oil shales are concerned the amounts of water available in the Colorado Basin are sufficient to process about a million barrels a day. It really seems inconceivable that one would bring down large quantities of water, presumably from Canada because they are already supplying California from the northern US states in that area. As far as the energy balance is concerned, I have not done detailed calculations, but I am sure there is a net gain in the processing and transportation of the liquid hydrocarbons. The amount of heat that you have to put in is quite small compared to the energy contained in the oil itself in the tar sands or heavy oil.

Mr W. C. R. Whalley (Iraq Petroleum Company): Do we now entirely reject the experience of the Germans and experience in this country in the 1930s–1940s? By the early 1940s the Germans had worked up to a production of about 150 000 barrels a day, ICI were operating a coal/oil plant in the 1930s and throughout the war. Are these no longer considered relevant?

Mr M. W. Clegg: I think it is considered that the process is grossly uneconomic now; this goes on in South Africa as well, with Sasol producing liquid fuel, but I think that unless the technology is improved it is too expensive. I believe the reason is that it is a high pressure process and the reactors are very small so you have to have very large numbers of them.

Mr N. White (Hambros Bank Ltd): First, could you give any indication of the relative investment cost per barrel of crude produced from Athabasca compared with conventional crude oil say, in the North Sea? Secondly, you implied in your paper that about 10% of Athabasca could be produced by surface mining—I presume the other 90% could be recovered by *in situ* methods and not deep mined. Thirdly, would you like to hazard a guess as to the 90%? What value would crude oil have to reach before that could become economic?

Mr M. W. Clegg: The capital investment required to develop the tar sands, I think, runs at the moment somewhere between four and five thousand dollars per barrel per day, which I think compares with around $2500 for the North Sea.

Mr G. Chandler (President, Institute of Petroleum): You are in fact producing something which does not need to be fully refined, and therefore is not wholly comparable?

Mr M. W. Clegg: The quality of the oil after it has been processed in Athabasca is a residue-free light distillate oil. I think probably in the case of Great Canadian it is a 38° API and in the case of syncrude it would be 34° API and will presumably, therefore, have a slightly higher value than the comparable North Sea crude.

In answer to the second question, I think this is a sort of figure which has acquired an unjustified standing in the industry—it is something which everybody now seems to quote and I think that a lot more work needs to be done in order to prove if it is indeed as much as 10% and of course the amount that can be surface mined, depends on current economics. It could well be that if oil prices go up substantially it would pay you to strip off three times as much overburden as oil sand. At the moment I think it is reckoned on a one-to-one basis—you take off 50 ft if you have 50 ft of pay sand.

As to whether or not the deeper sands are producible by *in situ* methods, I do not believe myself it would be logical to make a deduction that the other 90% are producible in that way, mainly because of problems of cap rock cover and the ability to inject hot fluids into the formation in order to reduce the viscosity.

I would think that when one got down below about 700–1000 ft one would then say that these deposits ought ultimately to be producible by *in situ* methods. The area in between I think will be very difficult and will probably have to be mined, but at the present time that does not look as if it will be economic for a long long time.

CHAPTER 10

Alternative Sources of Energy

A. R. UBBELOHDE, C.B.E., F.R.S.

Professor of Thermodynamics, Imperial College of Science and Technology, University of London, UK

My title is sufficiently general to support quite a major role as prophet, particularly if one carefully chooses vague self-neutralising prophecies. But if one wants to make really constructive forecasts about the future, one must take the risks of being specific. What are the directions in which one really must be specific, to be at all helpful? One must perforce pay even more attention to methods of distribution than to the prime generation of available energy.

ENERGY NETWORKS AND ENERGY PACKAGES

A broad distinction in my view is most usefully made between the future of energy networks and the future of energy packages. The locations of use of energy packages can be chosen much more flexibly, which gives them a special advantage. In other ways, too, though to some extent interdependent, developments in these two main ways of using energy are subject to very different social and economic pressures.

Unfortunately, the familiar tables of figures for overall energy consumption seldom, or never discriminate between the growth of use of energy through networks and that through packages. This incompleteness could become a serious limitation on sophisticated forecasting. As the cost of energy from various primary fuels increases, it is by no means evident that the ratio of total network to total package use will remain much the same as at present. Can anything be said about this? My first forecast of trends is that in advanced industrial and social structures network supplies of energy will continue to grow in importance relative to package supplies. Full technological control of energy generation by the fusion of light atomic nuclei, even when it comes, will, if anything, accelerate this general trend for energy networks. Again, use of efficiency-increasing methods such as magnetohydrodynamics will favour growth of energy networks by improving the efficiency of generating stations. On the other hand, there are added obstacles if the MHD units have to be easily mobile.

A second forecast is that very probably, because the cost of major changes can be broken down into much smaller quanta, innovations will be speedier and more spectacular in package uses. Before discussing such package uses,

153

one should look briefly at some of the rather more humdrum growth aspects of energy networks.

Any forecast about the relatively faster growth of energy uses through networks needs careful testing, since it is basic for the future of energy-hungry advanced communities. It assumes, inter alia, that disadvantageous aspects of energy packages, including rising production, transport and distribution costs, will escalate even faster than at present, tilting the relative balance ever more in favour of network uses.

ENERGY NETWORKS

In principle, one should consider the future of electricity grids separately from (in decreasing order of network range) grids of piped gaseous and liquid fuels and even of suitably fluidised solid fuels. The growth of natural gas networks seems assured so long as supplies are available. Though this is a matter of some importance to the petroleum industry it is premature to forecast whether the same established networks will, in due course, serve to distribute synthetic gaseous fuels. To be brief we may therefore concentrate on electricity generating stations. Other things being equal, network growth favours the survival and proliferation of generating stations of ever increasing sophistication, and of the highest efficiency. As a problem in forecasting, it is not clear to me to what extent this will also favour ever-increasing size of generating stations. A point must come where primary flow aspects of any electricity generating station, chiefly of fuel towards it, and of combustion products (not forgetting waste heat) away from it, must limit any efficiency advantages resulting from ever-increasing size. If a purely theoretical approach were ever relevant, no doubt general computerised solutions could be formulated for the problem of the ideal distribution of generating stations in any national network. It might be interesting to know how nearly such ideal computerised solutions match any existing national power grids. The formulation will, of course, differ according to the primary fuel whose use is being considered. Obviously, solid fuels impose severe transport constraints on the optimum network. Fluid fuels are much more adaptable, once flow line costs have been properly allowed for. Nuclear fuels would appear to present even smaller constraints on the optimum distribution of generating centres in an ideal power network. Optimisation considerations provide just one more reason for expecting constant increases in relative as well as total generation of energy from nuclear sources for network distribution. I am continually surprised that this change has till now been relatively so slow even in technologically advanced countries.

Before passing to package uses of energy, are there any primary sources whose development could distort in a major way trends forecast about networks?

SOLAR ENERGY

Some authorities speak impressively about our highly inefficient use of the regular income of solar energy constantly reaching the earth. But until energy starvation comes much closer, I do not think better use of our solar income could make much of a dent in the global annual energy users' budget. Enormous reserves of solar energy capital are conveniently concentrated geologically as coal or oil deposits. As energy becomes more costly, additional reserves of energy such as tar sands and shale will also become more attractive economically. Although the daily solar flux actually reaching the earth is very large in its totals (it has been estimated at about 10^{14} horsepower) its intensity is not very high, at best about 8·4 joules/square centimetre/minute. Compared with this, the total gross energy use in the United States of America in the year 1970 was nearly 7×10^{19} joules. It is further significant that the solar flux tends to be chancy, particularly in those highly industrialised parts of the globe where energy starvation is most threatening. Possibly more uses of solar energy will, in future, be developed in exceptionally favoured regions. Mass production can work wonders in reducing construction costs of the necessary contrivances. But in all, the earth's solar energy income does not at present seem hopeful as a major contribution for conventional domestic prime movers. Collective uses, particularly in the production of drinking water, may perhaps offer some help in favoured regions of the world where fresh water tends to be a high cost commodity. Of course, direct generation of electrical energy from solar energy might in principle be much more rewarding than any indirect uses of solar energy merely as heat. But, in practice, no cheap photo-electric generators have yet emerged. A nagging thought is that the volume of research dedicated to direct conversion of solar energy is (as yet) trifling compared with the enormous accumulation of research and development on conventional mechanical heat engines. If comparable effort had been made, would the relative positions still be as at present?

TIDAL POWER

Other optimists speak hopefully about the harnessing of tidal power. But tidal power is even more subject to geophysical peculiarities than the kindred water power, and development of water power demands very high capital costs. Though useful contributions to certain national energy budgets might emerge, neither form of water power could be expected to make further massive contributions to the world's energy budget.

MICRO-CLIMATES

Climatic factors already act as a load on energy network development in ways that are seldom clearly brought out in national energy budgets. In the ever more hungry energy future, the fraction of its total energy budget used by a nation merely to keep warm, or to keep cool by air conditioning, needs to be much more clearly estimated than at present. As one of the means of affecting the energy used to control micro-climates, major developments are likely to emerge in uses of materials for thermal insulation. Another more Jules Verne type of question about climates is whether different nations will ever agree sufficiently well politically to tinker co-operatively with the

Arctic regions, so as to ensure, for example, a reliable sequence of warm dry winters, whose incidence in most parts of the world is at present not under human control. Again, the abundant proliferation of really intense thunderclouds, by man-made weather changes, might possibly become a valuable source of climatic energy to be tapped, if the necessary political agreement could first be achieved.

ENERGY PACKETS

Energy networks, which are comparatively new in man's uses of inanimate energy, impose severe material and even political constraints on human behaviour by their inescapable dominance, as well as by their comparative inflexibility. By contrast, more happy-go-lucky uses of inanimate energy in mobile packets are as old as man. However, logs of wood or bags of coal for burning, or even cans of hydrocarbon fuels carried to mechanical prime movers as required are fast becoming obsolete, through high costs, or pollution hazards, or other novel factors arising from high population densities. Yet even in the more sophisticated future, the mobility and flexible use of energy packets must continue to give them great advantages. In my view, therefore, although there will be steady growth of energy distributing networks in relative as well as total importance, the more spectacular innovations in the next twenty five years are bound to lie in the development of much more sophisticated power packages. Both the prime movers and the fuels to nourish them, are under constant pressures, economic and social, and these pressures are likely to promote profound modifications of design and development. Additional deliberate pressures through differential taxation will, in my opinion, also become much more prominent than hitherto. (Up to the present, Treasury experts and politicians have had such uncertain views about our energy future that taxation pressures have not been used in any decisive way to promote changes, even when these are agreed to be necessary.)

Can one think about possible changes at all tidily? Can one hope, too, not to miss any jack-in-the-box novelties that will spring up when conventional fuels become, say, twice as expensive as now? We may conveniently group our considerations about the future of energy packages according to whether they are used in the more familiar happy-go-lucky ways, or whether their use as packages is linked to energy networks.

Energy packages not linked to energy networks
What can be forecast even now about

  (i) New prime movers
      (a) Mechanical.
      (b) Fuel cell and electrochemical prime movers generally.
      (c) Others such as small mobile magnetohydrodynamic units, or nuclear radiation batteries.
 (ii) The development of special fuels (including synthetic chemicals) to operate such prime movers?

Energy packages directly linked to energy networks
What can be forecast even now about

(i) Secondary cells and other electrochemical devices using stored energy.
(ii) Stored fuel gases such as hydrogen?

THE BUILD-UP OF ENERGY DEMAND

With hindsight, one can say that during the past one hundred years since the emergence of the Otto internal combustion engine, it is mainly the availability of cheap hydrocarbon fuels that has permitted build-up of such a fantastic demand situation for mobile uses of inanimate energy. This demand never would have been built up in the same way without cheap fuels. Fuels now seem bound to rise steadily in cost. However, because of the built-in energy demand of advanced communities, in many ways the momentum of uses now reached will probably persist. Our power needs, particularly in certain directions, will be self-perpetuating, even when hydrocarbon fuels become much more expensive through scarcity, and through restrictions on their use in conurbations because of pollution from cumbustion products. As an estimate, illustrative of the many that are being published, one may consider the United States' projected total demands for energy (Table 1).

TABLE 1
Projected Total Energy Demands (Joules $\times 10^{18}$) in the United States of America[a]

	1970	1975	1985	2000
Petroleum	31·4	38·3	50·3	70·2
Natural gas	23·9	30·4	41·8	53·6
Coal	14·6	17·1	23·6	27·8
Hydro	2·8	3·0	3·7	5·3
Nuclear	0·2	5·1	22·1	46·1

[a] More fully discussed in an article by A. R. Ubbelohde (1972) *Revue Soc. Roy. Belge des Ingenieurs et des Industriels*, p. 299.

In the absence of more precise information, we may assume that (say) half the first row of figures (*i.e.* for petroleum) corresponds with current energy-package uses. This helps to remind us how the evolution of the modern motor car has been conditioned by two factors, both of which are now obsolescent. On the one hand fuel has been comparatively very cheap, which has encouraged the production of expensive cars of relatively high horsepower. Their prestige is linked partly with their size. A second factor arises because large cars are at present relatively heavy. Table II gives some contemporary figures.

TABLE 2[a]

	Bhp	Kerb weight (lb)
Fiat 500(F)L	18	1 106
Reliant Regal 3/30	31	966
Citroen AMI 8	35	1 312
Honda N 600	38	1 191
Mini	38	1 360
Opel	54	1 642
Ford Escort	57	1 775
Austin 1300	60	1 844
MG Mk III	65	1 550
Moskvich	80	2 212
Audi	100	2 320
Mazda 616	100	2 020
Mercedes Benz	105	2 920
Chrysler USA	225	4 475
Daimler	245	3 703
Aston Martin	300	3 800
Bristol	335	3 775
AC 7017 cc	345	3 143

[a] Data from the Observers' Book of Automobiles, Frederick Warne and Company, 1972.

MATERIALS TECHNOLOGY

Of course, this need for weight has partly arisen from the need to design for safety when crashing into other mobile users of power; old fashioned materials such as iron and wood or even steel do weigh rather a lot for a given strength requirement. But now, we are certainly moving into an age where materials technology will favour use of adequately strong, but much lighter materials. In mobile units, these would combine well with power engines much lighter than have been customary. I foresee an era of mobile vehicles closer to the world of large insects than the world of large reptiles or mammals in power/weight/strength design concepts. The new materials are there waiting to be used; and the turn of the screw of energy scarcity and pollution control cannot fail to impose design and development of efficient engines of much smaller average horsepower than at present, housed in strong vehicles of the lowest possible weight. It should be appreciated that the more acceptable of future designs may not be very cheap and need not be very small. We form quite a wrong idea of how attractive they could be made from a few current very-low-powered cars, all of which tend to be at the cheapest end of the price range. Even now, in cases when very low construction cost is not the prime consideration, modern materials technology has some very attractive possibilities to offer, fully competitive with the heavy old-fashioned materials still mostly being used.

Such design forecasts seem wholly safe to make; all still assume that the incalculable advantages of easy mobility will continue to favour the use of liquid fuels as energy stores for mechanical prime movers, even though high fuel costs impose designs that offer much more prominent advantages in their high power/weight ratios. It is at this point that a real chasm of uncertainty can be designated in forecasting our energy future. Energy distributing networks are bound to grow enormously in any event. For linking to these networks, if only a light and economical secondary storage cell were to become available, the obvious attractions of being able to 'hook-on' storage cells to energy distributing networks at times of the day most economical for re-charging would revolutionise the types of successful energy packages that could emerge. Already, electric cars for urban use are benefiting from economic as well as social pressures—e.g. the 'Witkar' development linked to electricity grids in the city of Amsterdam. But, despite very considerable and certainly costly research, all commercially developed secondary cells at present have either unfavourable power to weight ratios, or unfavourable efficiency factors, or both. Is this chasm which arrests our potential evolution as sophisticated users of energy networks merely the consequence of so very many years of ridiculously cheap energy derived from hydrocarbon fuels, fending off any adequate financial incentives for much more massive programmes of research on secondary storage of energy? In this direction too, the screw might, in my view, with advantage be artificially tightened to promote more development of secondary storage in highly portable forms, instead of relying on the gradual cost increases of conventional liquid fuels to provide incentives for such development. With the greater use of secondary storage cells for mobile energy packages production of really light-weight electric motors would, no doubt, likewise receive much additional impetus.

SECONDARY STORAGE

I do not propose to say very much about secondary storage of energy through the production of electrolytic hydrogen. This would still leave open the question whether such hydrogen would be used to drive mechanical prime movers, or to generate electrical energy from fuel cells carried in mobile units. Apart from their possible role for secondary energy storage, development of really light-weight gas-storage cylinders might also favour 'hook-on' refuelling of mobile units based on natural gas networks. Again, this is a matter of modern materials technology. I am rather pessimistic, however, about hydrogen storage. Only a gipsy forecast seems possible along these lines at present.

Of course, direct electrochemical generation of energy may show much greater growth than can at present be rationally expected. With regard to fuel cells, advantages of electrochemical in place of thermal generation of the available energy in fuel molecules are well appreciated theoretically. Chemical thermodynamics must ever regard it as barbaric, first to randomise molecular chemical energy as heat, prior to converting only a fraction of such randomised energy back again into available energy by means of a mechanical heat engine. However, despite all such theoretical arguments, up to the present, practical difficulties have obstructed successful development of fuel cells except for high cost uses. Electrochemically satisfactory electrodes have been hard to design. The need to use electrolytes, either as solvents or molten salts, introduces further difficulties with all types of fuel cells yet described. Thermodynamic regrets about this comparative practical failure to master direct conversion of chemical into electrical available energy, should be tempered by the reflection that the number of man-years of inventive effort on fuel cells has as yet been wholly insignificant compared with the accumulated inventive effort on internal combustion engines using hydrocarbon fuels, stimulated by the ready availability and cheapness of liquid fuels.

DIRECT CONVERSION

Again, it is conceivable that nuclear radiation falling on suitable solids could generate voltage differences, to be used for generating electrical energy. However, direct conversion of nuclear energy into available energy without prior randomisation into heat seems remote, and has received little or no attention. As with other innovations in present uses of energy packages, it is arguable that we have been held back from direct conversion methods of all kinds by the fact that hydrocarbon fuels have been ultra-cheap. Should the cost of hydrocarbons for use as fuels continue to rise through scarcity and through pollution taxes, economic and social pressures will undoubtedly help boost research and design effort in all these novel directions.

SPECIAL LIQUID FUELS

More development of special liquid fuels may also help. Bulk production of chemicals of all kinds has already brought much nearer synthetic chemicals at moderate cost and of relatively high purity for consideration as easily transportable energy reserves, clean in use in any kind of mobile power unit, whether fuel cell or internal combustion engine. Methanol is an obvious example. At present it costs about £23 per ton which should however be compared with the users' price (including tax) for hydrocarbon fuels. In the United States of America its production has doubled in the last seven years and is now about 9×10^8 gallons. Subject to suitable designs whether of mechanical prime movers or of fuel cells the balance of advantages for energy packages may in the longer term possibly tilt away from hydrocarbon fuels in favour of such less pollution creating fuels.

NOVEL MATERIALS

Favourable future developments in regard to a basic human need such as that for abundant sources of inanimate energy call for the application of commercial, economic and political skills at the highest levels. Much of the foregoing strikes me as an educationist in a particular way. Major economies in the use of existing fuels, as well as developments in the harnessing of novel prime sources of energy, await the evolution of engineering designs that imply profound knowledge of the opportunities offered by novel materials.

Materials technology is a vital sector of knowledge for such designers. This is a hybrid educational discipline, since it calls for grasp of most of the important aspects of mechanical engineering, combined with an understanding of those molecular aspects of materials which can determine unique advantages in their behaviour, even under adverse conditions. For some years now, at Imperial College, we have been concerned with building up Advanced Courses in Materials Technology and in giving them to graduates already well versed in more conventional aspects, particularly of chemical or mechanical engineering. The availability of sufficient numbers of engineers properly aware of new opportunities with materials is one of the necessary conditions for more rapid progress in the development of alternative energy sources.

Discussion

Professor P. R. Odell (Erasmus University, Rotterdam): This is a question as to the analytical ability of dividing networks (energy grid systems) from package energy depending on networks of transport facilities. These are surely alternative distribution systems and their relative economics contribute to the choice of alternative energy sources for given geographical patterns of the demand for energy. Moreover, with a given geography of demand, different and alternative energy sources influence the optimisation of the network system.

Professor A. R. Ubbelohde: I think we are going to have to spend more and more on nuclear energy and other forms of 'immobile generation' of energy including generation from coal. And because they are immobile they are bound to involve distribution by networks, which will grow enormously. I think distribution by road packages, efficient though it is, is going to suffer very much by competition from network distribution. Unless you evaluate this difference between network and package distribution, I believe you'll miss taking some very important decisions.

The opportunity of using alternative input fuels has an effect upon the optimisation of a network, in that it provides a parameter or restricted term in computer calculations. But it is least notable in a small bulk fuel like plutonium, and is largest with coal which you have to use fairly close to where it is produced. In any case I want to stress that any form of generation through networks is going to grow in my opinion enormously relative to packages, because of the immobility of many modern centres of generation. I can't conceive that a giant road tanker bounding along a country road is going to have much future, for example.

Mr C. L. Goodacre (Consultant): You undoubtedly know the Ford Company did a very deep investigation on the world's most efficient vehicles. Being in the transportation business, they are very conscious of the inefficiency of the transportation they produce. They came out with the answer that the most efficient vehicle in transportation is a bicycle because it has the highest thermal efficiency of any vehicle known. It is a first class example of where man gives nature a smack in the eye, but unfortunately this argument neglects one thing—that people are fundamentally lazy and they like to pay for means of transportation in which they have to do nothing except steer.

Mr G. Chandler (President, Institute of Petroleum): I merely wish to reinforce something Professor Ubbelohde said about insulation. One can in fact treat insulation as a form of exploration for oil, because one can directly equate cooling space of a house and insulation to barrels of oil. It clearly makes eminent sense to use some means of encouraging this—whether by fiscal means or others does not matter, but it would increase our energy supply.

163

Mr J. G. Mills: In the USA the trend is towards heavier, stronger and presumably safer cars to combat Naderism and the environmental aspect concerned with reduction in lead content of gasoline to enable after burners to be used. Is not this trend going in the wrong direction in that it increases the consumption of hydrocarbons?

Professor A. R. Ubbelohde: Yes indeed. The lead story arose because the people who did research on knock knew more about flame chemistry than they did about other forms of preventing knock. I myself had a certain amount to do with it so I know that if you are going to try and mitigate knock and keep to the relatively cheap hydrocarbon fuels which are so strongly entrenched, you may have to accept the solution of after burning to accompany existing versions of packaged fuels. However, I am seriously suggesting that one should not just do this. One should also estimate what would happen if we insisted on people using methanol (at £23 a ton) and gave them fiscal differences, or charged high prices for the use of hydrocarbon fuels without after burning, and make any extra weight so expensive to carry around that a light-weight engine using methanol or similar fuel in a light-weight car designed with an eye to strength would weather through financially.

Part of the trouble is that the people designing for strength at the moment don't know about, or are not thinking about, strength except associated with weight, and they don't know about or think about combustion except associated with cheap hydrocarbon fuels. This may not be the only answer. There may be a complete diversion in another direction. This is my purpose of encouraging more than one way at looking at these problems. That is why I am absolutely emphatic that we mustn't only look at the familiar tables and diagrams of global energy uses of coal and oil—we must also try and break them down into important subgroups of uses and then get good innovative designers.

Professor A. Williams (University of Leeds): Whilst the need for extractive processes leading to the formation of oil is appreciated, it seems strange that little or no attention has been paid to the gasification of oil sands and shales. In the long term this seems an attractive process since, although a low quality fuel may be produced, it is readily distributed and makes less demand on supplies of water. Furthermore, it can be reprocessed to liquid fuels or used directly. Is work anticipated in this field in the future?

Mr M. W. Clegg (British Petroleum Co. Ltd): I think at the moment it is purely a question of economics. The value of the products of gasifying the oils would be so much less than the value of the equivalent liquid fuel you could produce. I am not really aware of any work going on as far as tar sands are concerned.

CHAPTER 11

Towards the All-Electric Economy

L. G. BROOKES

United Kingdom Atomic Energy Authority, London, UK

First note the use of the word 'towards'. I think it will be a very long time before the energy economy is all electric. But I am sure the electricity component will increase steadily towards a very high proportion. Why do I say we are moving towards a very high electricity component in the energy economy? The answer is: partly because it is actually happening and partly because it will have to happen.

THE DEMAND FOR ELECTRICITY

Over the years, electricity has inexorably penetrated the general energy market. Both the total amounts of crude fuel inputs devoted to electricity and electricity's share of total useful* energy at the point of final consumption have steadily increased. Figure 1 shows the percentage of fuel devoted to electricity production in the UK in 10 year steps since 1920. Figure 2 shows the growth of electricity's share of useful energy at the point of consumption. Experience in other countries has been similar. It is interesting that in the early days this pattern of steady growth continued despite serious economic setbacks. Figure 3 shows that although coal production and consumption fell off sharply in the inter-wars slump, electricity continued to prosper. From 1920 to 1965 electricity consumption increased fifty fold.

The growth of electricity consumption has taken place despite an apparently very large unfavourable price differential. On a heat-supplied basis—therm for therm—oil costs the average industrial user about 3p/therm, coal about the same and electricity about 20p, ratios of 1:1:7. But 15 years ago the ratios were 1·3:1:10. For the future with an increasingly large nuclear component in national electricity systems, electricity will be more robust against fuel price increases than other forms of energy. If oil prices at the port double and other costs stay the same the cost of oil to the final consumer rises by about 80%. To bring about the same percentage increase in the price of nuclear fuelled electricity, the price of uranium ore would have to go up by a factor of over 20 for thermal reactors; and over 100 for fast reactors.

* Adams and Miovic[1] gave the following relative usefulness co-efficients for fuels in common use; direct use of coal 0·31; direct use of oil 0·76; electricity 0·84.

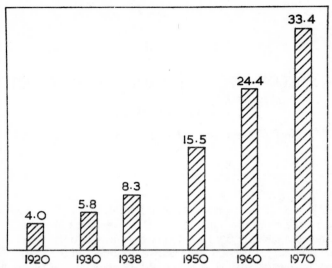

Fig. 1. Percentage of crude fuel input devoted to electricity production in the UK (1920–1970). (By courtesy of the United Kingdom Atomic Energy Authority.)

These differences are due partly to the very low absolute cost of nuclear fuel, but also to the fact that a large part of nuclear-fuelled electricity cost is capital cost. The need to find large amounts of capital for nuclear power has been something of a disadvantage up to now, but all forms of energy are calling more and more for a large injection of capital so this disadvantage to electricity in general and nuclear electricity in particular will become less marked.

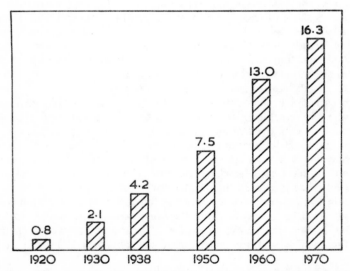

Fig. 2. Percentage electricity share of total UK useful energy consumption (1920–1970)· (By courtesy of the United Kingdom Atomic Energy Authority.)

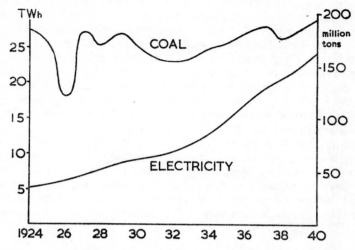

FIG. 3. Inter-war patterns of coal and electricity consumption in the UK. (By courtesy of the United Kingdom Atomic Energy Authority.)

TABLE 1

Elasticities of Demand for Electricity in the UK[a]

Industry group	Output elasticity of demand	Elasticity wrt Electricity price
		Price of other fuels
Food, drink, tobacco	2·571	−0·415[b]
Chemicals	0·821	−1·069
Non-ferrous metals	1·310	−0·843[b]
Iron and steel	1·507	−2·257[b]
Engineering	0·944	−0·588
Vehicles	1·216	−1·428[b]
Shipbuilding	−0·615[b]	−0·904[b]
Metals n.e.s.	0·647	−2·277
Textiles	1·307	−1·651
Leather and fur	0·301[b]	−2·532[b]
Clothing	0·162[b]	−2·444[b]
Timber	0·181[b]	−3·181[b]
Bricks	0·721	−0·738
Paper	0·746	−1·083
Other manufacturing	1·206	−1·207[b]
Mining and quarrying	−1·954	−2·017

[a] *See* reference 2 for the source of this table.
[b] The coefficient from which the elasticity was derived is not significant at the 0·95 level.

The demand for electricity has not in fact been very price sensitive, whereas consumer choice between the other fuels, especially industrial consumer choice, is very price sensitive.* So electricity can survive price increases better than the other fuels can. Now that industrial use of centrally generated electricity forms a higher proportion of the total, consumption is much more sensitive to the state of the economy than it used to be. Table 1 shows why. All the major industries have output elasticities of demand substantially greater than one. So, as industrial output expands, a higher and higher proportion of electricity consumption becomes due to a sector for which demand is sensitive to the state of the economy.

The figures I have given are for the UK, but over the world as a whole electricity consumption has been increasing at two to three times the rate of growth of consumption of all energy. Electricity's progress has been in all of the three main sectors—domestic, commercial and community, and industrial. Before we can say much about the future of electricity we must examine these sectors individually—past performance and future prospects.

DOMESTIC ELECTRICITY CONSUMPTION

Domestic electricity consumption has exhibited all the classic features of a luxury 'good' that gradually becomes more and more within the pocket of the ordinary man. This is very largely because the items on which domestic electricity is used—electric heaters, washing machines, deep freezers—also have this property. This would account for the robustness of electricity against the vicissitudes of the 1929/1930 slump—consumption was then only a small fraction of today's level and was concentrated in the hands of consumers whose spending power was not greatly or immediately sensitive to the state of the economy.

This thought prompted us, in the UKAEA, to attempt correlations between various economic parameters and domestic electricity consumption. We found that the best correlation was between personal disposable income and expenditure on electricity—once again showing that spending money on electricity is part of affluent consumption, even though some part of it might be regarded as necessary expenditure, e.g. for a minimum standard of lighting. This leads to the conclusion that the pattern of growth in domestic electricity consumption might be related to the log-normal curve of distribution of incomes. Let me remind you of its shape (Fig. 4). If we now assume that the price of electricity-consuming goods and the electricity bill of the present-day wealthy member of society steadily become smaller and smaller proportions of the average man's income (because prices come down by the 'learning' process while his income rises), then we would expect present day wealthy levels of consumption to be exhibited progressively by the blocks to the centre and left of the curve. If the progression along the horizontal axis is smooth then the typical 'S' curve growth pattern will ensue.

* Baxter and Rees[2] noted that the price elasticity of demand for electricity was not significant. But the output elasticity and the disposable income elasticity were high.

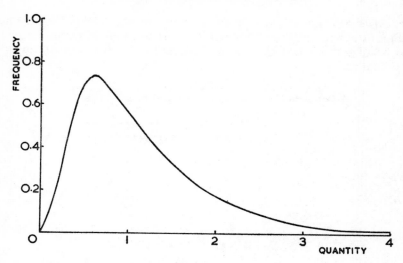

FIG. 4.   The log-normal distribution. (By courtesy of the United Kingdom Atomic Energy
Authority.)

A study of the likely future pattern of consumption was commissioned by
the UKAEA a year or so ago. Analysis of some detailed figures available for
the year 1966 produced the interesting comparisons shown in Table 2.

A small proportion of even larger and higher quality houses already have
air conditioning and make heavy use of lighting for architectural effect. Their

TABLE 2

Domestic Consumption per Annum kWh

	Average	Upper decile (approx.)
Lighting	450	1 000
Cooking	530	1 500
Water heating	910	1 500
Space heating and misc.	800	1 000
Washing machines	160	1 000
Refrigerator	230	650
Freezer	20	1 000
Total	3 100	7 650

consumption averages about 9000 kWh per annum. The split between the
standard social classes in 1966 was as shown in Table 3.

There are plenty of examples of the standards of the wealthy sector of
society becoming almost general in one generation, *e.g.* car, house and
television ownership. If the same pattern is followed for electricity consumption—with the wealthy continuing to increase their standards—though
possibly more slowly—then we can expect a very large increase in domestic
electricity consumption to have taken place by say 2000 AD. On top of this

there might be major increases in community use—standards of lighting and heating in public buildings, pumping to meet water distribution demands, road heating at accident black spots, electric buses, sewage treatment—the list is endless.

TABLE 3
Domestic Consumption of Standard Social Classes

Class	Proportion of consumers, %	Average annual consumption, kWh
AB	14·4	5 340
C1	19·9	3 780
C2	29·5	3 000
DE	36·2	2 050

COMMERCIAL CONSUMPTION

Similar considerations apply to commercial use—shops and offices. Standards are steadily rising, and some shops in particular—department stores and supermarkets—have very high standards of lighting and air conditioning with individual shops having demands at or approaching megawatt levels. The trend towards larger shops and supermarkets and the spread of air conditioning (already standard in new premises in London) could produce very large increases in demand. The ordinary man's growing interest in his living and working environment and the pressures of trade unions will see to it that standards in work-places also rise. Again we need only postulate existing minority high standards becoming general with some further improvement at the top end to see very large increases in consumption in this sector.

INDUSTRIAL CONSUMPTION

I have already mentioned the high output elasticities of electricity consumption in industry, *i.e.* the ratios between percentage rate of electricity consumption and percentage rate of growth of the industry itself. The pattern is different from industry to industry. For some the increase simply reflects higher standards of heating, lighting and ventilation in work-places; in others it reflects substitution of electrical aids for manual work; in others an evolutionary pattern of change to more modern electricity based methods; and finally, for some, revolutionary changes—such as the use of electric furnaces in the steel industry and electric kilns in the pottery industry.

A large part of the increase simply reflects high growth of industries that are heavy users of electricity—such as aluminium and chemicals production. Before we can speak of something approaching an all-electric economy, however, some major developments are necessary:

(i) More emphasis on higher temperature processes—say 800 to 1000°C. High temperatures can easily be provided by electrical means and such a switch would give a fillip to the industrial use of electricity.

(ii) More study of the technology of electro-heat generally. The Electricity Council Laboratories have been studying the use of electricity in metal-melting, but about 45% of all non-electrical energy used in industry is for low temperature processes—150 to 200°C—often calling for process steam. Electricity must penetrate this market if it is to gain a much larger share of industrial energy use.

Some developments naturally favour electricity. The most obvious one is the effect of rising labour cost and growing unreadiness to work inconvenient shift hours. This is likely to lead to a greater degree of automation in industry and this will favour the use of electricity. Another possible development would be the spread of chemical processes that exploit electricity more or less directly—using electrical energy to bring about chemical change. The most obvious example is the electrolysis of water, but the technique could be used more widely; and it is claimed that it would permit the use of very dilute sources of materials. Professor Fleichmann of Southampton University gave a paper on this subject at an IEE Symposium held on 8th May, 1970 in London. At the same symposium, Dr Churchman, the Director of the Electricity Council Research Laboratories, suggested other ways in which electricity might be used directly in industry—such as the elimination of the iron-making stage in steel production, producing refined steel directly in an arc furnace.

The *Electrical Times* for March 15th this year had a large section—focus on process heating—that described a number of ways in which electricity was being used for process heat in industry—in a mini steel works, in high-powered electric arc furnaces, in lamp ovens, and in induction furnaces for metal melting. The same issue described Loughborough University's new course in electro-heat—a very important development since it is a prerequisite of a large increase in the industrial use of electricity that there should be an adequate number of engineers of all types, knowledgeable about its possibilities.

THE NEED FOR ELECTRICITY

The demand for energy of all types is strongly correlated with the level of economic activity. The relationship is not a simple proportional one but it is nevertheless quite firm and well validated. For those who are interested, the validation is given in an article in the November 1972 issue of the *Journal of Industrial Economics*.[3] Figures 5 and 6 show the relationship both on a cross-section basis (connecting countries in widely different stages of development) and on a through-time basis for the UK. The method was applied to all regions of the world to produce an estimate of the requirement for useful energy on the basis of United Nations forecasts of population growth and a credible range of assumptions about future GNP growth—region by region, and, in some cases, country by country. GNP growth was not assumed to continue exponentially; each region (or country) was treated on its merits and considerable flattening was incorporated in the projections. The result for the world as a whole is shown graphically in Fig. 7. The increase is very considerable—by a factor of $3\frac{1}{2}$ to $5\frac{1}{2}$ by 2000 AD and by 10 to 20 by 2030 AD. These estimates are in terms of useful energy. That is to say they make allowance for the fact that oil is a more efficient fuel than coal (therm for therm) in terms of its contribution to economic output; and electricity is more efficient than either of them.

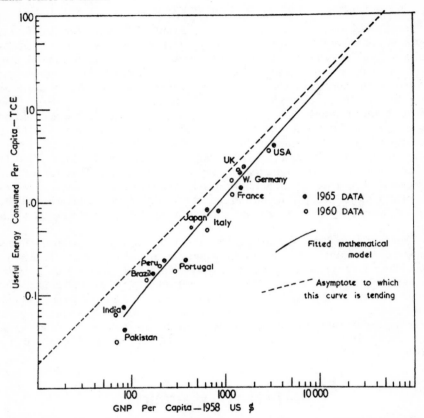

FIG. 5. Relationship between useful energy consumed per capita and GNP per capita. (By courtesy of the United Kingdom Atomic Energy Authority.)

There is no doubt that the traditional fuels could meet this pattern of demand for some time to come. But it would mean raising production considerably above what appears to be the present trend. It is very hard to be categoric about this, but there is considerable evidence for a natural life cycle of production of an exhaustible resource like those postulated by M. King Hubbert in Fig. 8. This shape follows from the hypothesis that as time goes on it becomes necessary to work the less accessible more expensive reserves; the higher costs and greater difficulty inevitably lead to a lower rate of production. There is also the point that rising prices encourage the introduction of substitutes and these may gradually take over from the existing product. If Hubbert's estimates are multiplied by the appropriate usefulness coefficients and aggregated the lower lines in Fig. 7 result. This indicates

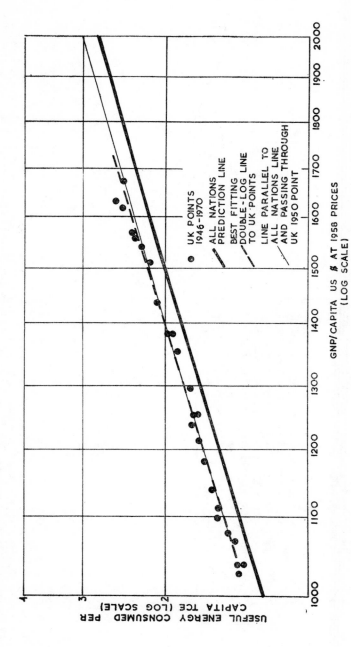

FIG. 6. Energy and economic growth, UK 1946–1970. (By courtesy of the United Kingdom Atomic Energy Authority.)

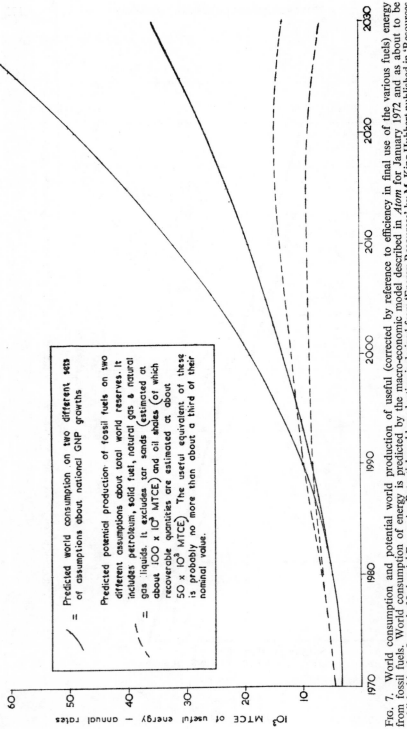

FIG. 7. World consumption and potential world production of useful (corrected by reference to efficiency in final use of the various fuels) energy from fossil fuels. World consumption of energy is predicted by the macro-economic model described in *Atom* for January 1972 and as about to be published in the *Journal of Industrial Economics*. Potential world production is derived from 'Energy Resources' by M. King Hubbert published in 'Resources and Man' by the US National Academy of Sciences and National Research Council. Excess of supply over demand in the early part of the period may reflect the use of some premium fuels—*e.g.* natural gas; in non-premium uses; or, more simply, consumption below the natural growth rate, level of production. (By courtesy of the United Kingdom Atomic Energy Authority.)

that—if Hubbert is right—the traditional sources of fossil fuels will fairly soon cease to meet the energy requirements that follow from quite modest aspirations about economic growth throughout the world.

However, the picture is not quite so simple as this. If, because of increased affluence, consumers of all types are able to absorb higher prices for energy for any given application, then the rate of extraction of the traditional fuels might be stepped up; and it might become economic to work the low grade sources such as the tar sands and oil shales. There might also be moves towards the production of oil and synthetic natural gas from coal—which I suggest is unlikely to enjoy any sustained growth in demand in its traditional form, partly because of consumer choice but also because rising world

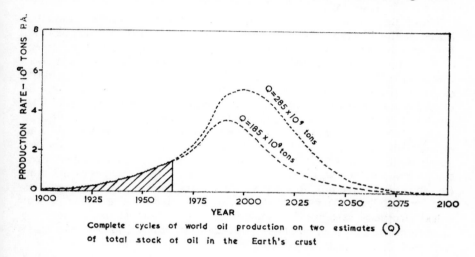

Complete cycles of world oil production on two estimates (Q) of total stock of oil in the Earth's crust

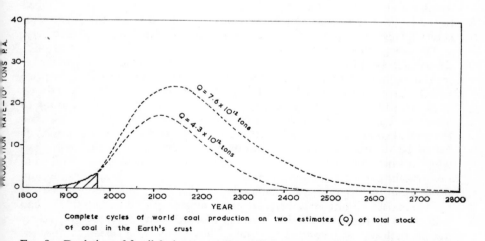

Complete cycles of world coal production on two estimates (Q) of total stock of coal in the Earth's crust

FIG. 8. Depletion of fossil fuel reserves. Top: oil, bottom: coal. Source: Report of the Committee on Resources and Man commissioned by the US Academy of Sciences, 1968. (By courtesy of the United Kingdom Atomic Energy Authority.)

labour costs will count against a predominately labour intensive form of fuel.

Even if we assume that as much as one half of the gap between the predicted demand and Hubbert's predictions of supply is met by stepping up fossil fuel output from traditional and non-traditional sources, there is still a very large requirement left which—at the moment—can only be filled by hydro and nuclear electricity. At 2000 AD this calls for a total of about 6000 GW of hydro and nuclear plant to have been installed in the world, growing at the rate of about 250 GW per annum. Hydro electricity accounts for only about 200 GW in the world and practical limitations on further exploitation suggest setting the upper limit at 600 GW. The requirement in 2000 AD for nuclear electricity is therefore about 5400 GW.

Thus it seems that future requirements for energy can be met at reasonable prices, but it will almost certainly mean a fairly high proportion of the demand being met in the form of electricity. This need present no very serious problem if the pattern of penetration by electricity that is already evident continues, this alone will go a long way to equate supply and demand for energy in the electrical sectors. In addition, studies that have been conducted—in the UKAEA and elsewhere—suggest that synthetic portable fuels could be produced at prices that would be acceptable for premium uses. Some of the methods of production might call for electrical energy but there should be no difficulty in meeting the additional demand with nuclear power. There are ample stocks of nuclear fuel in the world. If breeder reactors are used, even the presently identified, reasonably cheap (up to $15/lb) reserves of uranium (totalling over three million tons) would last the world for several centuries with an entirely nuclear electricity system ten times the size of the present world electricity system. If fusion reactors follow—most likely using the deuterium/tritium cycle, employing lithium as an intermediary—once again the fuel supplies are ample for centuries.

The sources of energy that are often mentioned for the more distant future —solar and geothermal energy for example—are also most easily supplied in the form of electricity. So, once again, the indicators are towards a substantially higher proportion of energy being consumed in the form of electricity.

The swing to electricity will of course be moulded to a large extent by price developments. Although counter influences can be quoted—and the movement in the short term is very hard to judge—it seems inevitable that the price of oil (currently the world's most important fuel) will rise significantly by 1985. United States, EEC and Japanese imports together will amount to about $2\frac{1}{2}$ times the present total output of the Middle East; and by this time the Middle East output will constitute 75% of the world's oil supply. It would be surprising if prices were not pushed up as far as they will go— which means up to the point where it becomes profitable to produce oil from non-traditional sources like coal and oil shale—say a factor of 2 to 3 up on the present world price. As mentioned earlier, demand for electricity is growing apace despite an apparently unfavourable price differential. The gap is likely to narrow considerably both because electricity costs are only partly due to fuel and will become very much less so as the nuclear component increases; and because prices of nuclear fuel are unlikely to rise as rapidly as prices of other fuels.

TECHNOLOGICAL, ORGANISATIONAL AND FINANCIAL/ ECONOMIC PROBLEMS

The balance between portable and non-portable fuels has already been mentioned. As fossil fuel prices rise there will inevitably be some tendency to specialisation in their use. In addition, we have seen that estimates of the costs of production of synthetic portable fuels make them acceptable for those uses for which portability is essential—all forms of transport for example. In the more distant future the development of high energy density, rapid charging batteries, introduces another form of portability. Thus, a high proportion of electricity in the primary energy system need not cause any problems on the score of the balance between portable and non-portable forms of energy.

Much electricity used in industry is for peripheral applications like lighting, heating, ventilation and rotary power. But there are already enough examples of electricity's direct use in production processes to show that there is no reason why it should not be economic as the major energy input to production; its use is spreading—the steel and pottery industries have been mentioned, and much work is being done to show that electricity could be used even more widely. Perhaps one of the most important developments is the introduction of the Loughborough course in electro-heat. Once the engineering profession become convinced about the scope for large scale use of electricity in industry it could penetrate quite quickly—especially as price relativities become more favourable. Modern trends towards automation and improvements in working conditions are also likely to favour electricity as a solution to industrial problems. Except for a substantial part of the space heating market, developments in the other sectors—domestic and commercial—are already in favour of electricity; and as price relativities change, and consumers feel more able to pay for convenience, electricity will gain more of the space heating market.

Fears have been expressed about the availability of capital to meet large programmes of investment in electrical power—including nuclear power— and investment in the necessary industrial plant for conversion to electrical methods of production. The fact is that energy generally is becoming more capital intensive. The oil industry has a perpetual problem of making provision for capital for prospecting, production, transport and refining. This is no different in kind from the capital necessary to increase the size of electrical systems and provide the plant for making use of the electricity. If the operation is profitable, then capital will be forthcoming just as for any other project. In economic terms the problem is one of devoting enough of the nations resources to capital goods as distinct from consumption goods. If countries achieve the hoped-for growth in output there should be sufficient margin of resources to provide for the appropriate capital investment. Just as for any other form of investment, if the nation is not prepared to make adequate provisions the rate of growth of productive resources will slow down and planned growth levels will not be achieved. The danger lies in failing to appreciate that resources must be devoted to investment in energy— almost above all other forms of investment—if economic growth is to be sustained. The growth in productive resources that follows from achieving the proper balance between consumption and investment and—within the capital sector—between the various types of investment sees to it that resources exist to continue the process if society has a mind to continue it.

ACKNOWLEDGEMENT

Any views expressed or implied in this paper are the author's own and not those of the UK Atomic Energy Authority, whose permission to publish this paper is acknowledged.

REFERENCES

1. F. G. Adams and P. Miovic (1968). 'On relative fuel efficiency and the output elasticity of energy consumption in Western Europe', *Journal of Industrial Economics*, **XVII**(1), 41.
2. R. E. Baxter and R. Rees (1968). 'Industrial use of electricity', *Economic Journal*, **LXXVIII**(310).
3. L. G. Brookes (1972). 'More on the output elasticity of energy consumption', *Journal of Industrial Economics*, **XXI**(1), 83.
4. M. K. Hubbert (1969). 'Energy resources' in *Resources and Man*, US National Academy of Sciences.

Discussion

Mr R. W. Cooke (Central Electricity Generating Board): Would the speaker comment on the practicability of reducing the consumption of domestic electrical energy for heating (as has been suggested by other speakers) bearing in mind (a) that technically it is unlikely that generating equipment will be able to respond to the sort of load factors and load profile that would result if there was no domestic heating load, (b) that environmentally the most acceptable manner of burning the large quantities of fossil fuel (and indeed nuclear fuel) is in a large power station complex and (c) that we would only be using the large capital investment (itself a scarce resource) in generating equipment for some 20% of its potentially useful life.

Mr L. G. Brookes: It would be a pity to discourage the use of electricity. It's something people want, it's obviously one of the ways in which people like to spend their increased affluence. If people are prepared to pay to buy on peak electricity, charge them for it. The other problem is that if you discourage the use of electricity, then you will not get the growth in system demand which will give you the opening to have nuclear power. I am arguing that time isn't on our side, and if we are to make our energy economy robust against future price increases, we want to start getting some nuclear power in now. The problem is that recent setbacks in growth have meant that very few nuclear power stations have been ordered. I don't think it matters very much whether you've got load factors less than 100%. Unless you've got some method of storing energy, the capital cost is warranted. I don't really quite see the difficulty.

Mr G. Chandler (President, Institute of Petroleum): I am a little surprised at the historical picture and the assertions of the efficiency of electricity. I appreciate the extreme private enterprise attitude on the part of Mr Brookes that what people want and can pay for they should have. At the same time I think we need to be interested in waste, whatever the situation of energy supply. My understanding is that the use of fossil fuel electricity for heating houses, for example, is grossly inefficient compared with the use of coal or oil directly. I think these are very important factors and that they are greatly glossed over in Mr Brooke's presentation.

Mr L. G. Brookes: I am talking about secondary fuels. I think the efficiency of electrical heating in the terms of the amount of heat you get out for the therms you put in is very high. I was trying to account for the attractiveness of electricity despite its high price and I am now merely regarding electricity as a fuel. I think electricity's efficiency often gets undervalued. The fact that people can switch it on and off when they want it may mean it has a hidden efficiency of its own that often gets underestimated.

179

Mr R. G. Whorrod (Imperial Continental Gas Association): I can give you one reason for the desirability of electricity and that is subsidy. I believe the electricity industry in this country is being subsidised a great deal and that is why electricity is still cheap.

Mr J. M. C. Bishop (Phillips Petroleum Co. Ltd): In view of the need to invest in distribution grids for electricity and the fact that natural gas distribution networks are currently being expanded rapidly throughout Europe, has thought been given to the use of nuclear power, especially off peak, for the generation of hydrogen which could be distributed through what by that time will probably be a gas system that has run out of gas?

Mr L. G. Brookes: As you say, we've invested a lot of money in a gas grid and we've given quite a lot of encouragement to the industry and to the public to use natural gas. In fact, we've done just what the Americans did—the Americans boosted their gas sales, they are now in the position of having to try and maintain the gas supplies to meet their obligations to gas users. I think before the end of the century it is quite likely that we shall be producing synthetic natural gas, and pumping it down the gas lines. I don't know whether this will be met to any extent by hydrogen. The applications I have heard of for hydrogen are in things like air transport, but my personal view is that once you have established a market and have invested in some large network then you are under an obligation to meet the customers' demands.

With regard to subsidy: I am not sure where the subsidy for electricity consumers comes in except in the form of the subsidisation of the coal industry. The electricity consumers get some of their electricity produced by subsidised coal, but if you talk to the Generating Board they would rather be allowed to use oil, if they had a free choice. As a general rule, the Generating Board act to cover their costs—they have an obligation to do this.

Mr R. G. Whorrod: My point is that at the moment they don't, by a long way, and somebody's making up the difference and will continue to make up the difference until the price of electricity reflects the true costs.

Mr L. G. Brookes: It has reflected true costs until fairly recently, and I think the Generating Board would like to put the price up, but are not allowed to at the moment. All they are doing, therefore, is accumulating a deficit and my understanding of the situation is that they will have to recover this in due course with higher prices.

I suspect that the tariff is a bit unbalanced and I think the domestic consumers get their electricity too cheaply and industrial consumers pay too much. But I think overall the planning of the industry is to recover all their costs including a return on their capital.

Professor P. R. Odell (Erasmus University, Rotterdam): (a) Mr Brookes' paper shows no concern for the 'wasteful' use of energy by consumers able to do exactly what they like within the framework of this purchasing power ability. Has discussion here this week not persuaded him to change his mind about this attitude? (b) With regard to the GNP/energy-use relationship. Does his extrapolation of energy use to 2030 imply a continuation of this positive (at least) relationship for the richest economies even when they get to per capita income levels at a multiple of 6000+ per annum?

Mr L. G. Brookes: Taking the second point first. This was in fact a postulated relationship. If you remember there was a certain amount of prior argument which said it would fall to a one-to-one relationship and not below; and it was based of course on useful energy. If in fact somebody finds some step function method of making energy more useful, then my coefficients would have to be adjusted. The fact that I can use my method derives from the fact that these coefficients do seem to be stable over quite long periods. Obviously they have to be reviewed from time to time to see if they are still sound. But on the general line, I am not saying that GNP per head throughout the world must go on increasing for ever and ever. It will come up against some constraint possibly on the supply of some resource, maybe energy itself, and when it does, the growth in energy demand will slow down as well.

Professor P. R. Odell: But no constraint had been written into your curve through to 2030 in terms of US/Europe/Japan such as, say, getting to $18 000/$20 000 per capita and stopping there?

Mr L. G. Brookes: That constraint only came in the projection of economic growth rates. I assumed they wouldn't be maintained—certainly the countries of very high growth rates couldn't maintain them, and those where they have already achieved high GNP per capita certainly wouldn't go on rising all that rapidly, probably because they reach a point where the community doesn't seem to demand higher material standards with quite the same fervour.

On the other point, I do agree with the view that the world has lavish supplies of energy and uses them lavishly. On this question of the importance of saving energy, I think we must really keep a perspective. If you worked yourself blue in the face improving efficiency in the use of energy you would be unlikely to improve it by a factor of, say, more than two. So if you achieve this throughout the whole world energy economy then you postpone any energy crisis by one fuel use doubling time, which is perhaps 10–12 years. If you think you're running up against some sort of dynamic problem that you can't get alternative sources of energy in quickly enough, it may well pay you to spend a lot of money and capital equipment to save energy, to buy that extra 10–12 years.

CHAPTER 12

The Middle East Exporting Countries and the International Petroleum Industry

EDITH PENROSE

Professor of Economics, School of Oriental and African Studies,
University of London, UK

THE CHANGING SCENE

The purpose of this paper is to examine the position and policies of seven oil-producing countries of the Middle East and North Africa—Iran, Saudi Arabia, Kuwait, Iraq, Abu Dhabi, Libya and Algeria—with respect to their significance for the supply and price of oil and for the future role of the international companies and OPEC in the area. The governments of these countries have now obtained a control that they have long demanded but never before achieved not only over the tax-paid cost of crude oil but over total offtake as well. The bargaining position of the international companies has collapsed to such an extent that they seem to have little scope left for independent action. Nevertheless, bargaining must still take place and we must recognise that there are limits to the extent to which the exporting countries can press their advantage. Indeed, just as the oil companies made important concessions to their host governments when the latter were relatively weak in order to maintain a minimum of good will, so may the exporting countries now make concessions in recognition of the problems of the importing countries and of companies, which relate primarily to the continuity and security of supply and to the cost of oil. The exporting countries also have objectives of their own the achievement of which can be jeopardised by imprudent action. We shall explore these issues.

FROM SURPLUS TO SCARCITY?

The shift of the bargaining advantage suddenly and heavily to the side of the exporting countries has been associated with and intensified by a sudden fear of 'scarcity'. As late as 1970 it was still fashionable to speak of an 'oil surplus'; within less than two years an 'oil crisis' became fashionable. But what is this crisis? Technically, of course, just as a surplus is merely excess supply at current prices and therefore falling prices, so scarcity is merely excess demand at current prices and therefore rising prices. But this is not a 'crisis' situation, and the concern now being expressed is not simply that oil is going to become scarcer in the more distant future and prices must therefore rise in anticipation of it.

It is rather an expression of fear of a situation in which prices are expected to rise in the relevant planning period—say 15 years—not only so high that significant existing uses will have to be cut back severely because they can no longer bear the cost, but also so fast that appropriate adjustments cannot be made reasonably smoothly and severe dislocation will follow. Such a situation could conceivably arise in two circumstances. First if costs of production—the unit costs of finding and developing oil resources—were to rise very rapidly and unexpectedly; secondly if producers with control over supply were able rapidly to force up prices to the point at which such dislocation was threatened.

There seems to be universal agreement that the first of these is not the cause of the problem at present—indeed, it is unlikely ever to cause a crisis since a real 'physical scarcity' would be expected long in advance of its arrival. Known reserves capable of being developed at little above existing costs are universally agreed to be more than adequate to meet all expected demands over the next 15 to 20 years. Around 1995 the picture is of course much more clouded and geological experts disagree.

It is also universally agreed, however, that the second set of circumstances is a clear possibility. The major exporting countries, by the mere threat to use their collective monopoly power, have been able to push up taxes and other costs for the companies, and there is some fear that they will carry this so far and so fast as to create a crisis for the consuming countries, in spite of the fact that it is not their intention to bring this about.

A fear of shortage in this sense is to be distinguished from insecurity of supply—a fear that oil might simply be denied by the suppliers. The two are, of course, related and one can lead to the other. To gain a strongly resisted increase in payments from the companies, governments may threaten to cut supplies to recalcitrant companies, and this has implications for consuming countries. The power to withhold supplies is an inherent aspect of monopoly power, as Professor Adelman has cogently pointed out, but the likelihood of its exercise requires analysis.

I shall now consider each of the seven countries as a source of reliable supplies for the major consuming countries. There are two types of consideration: the importance of the supply from a given country, which is a function of the amount of oil it is now exporting and the amount it is expected to be able to deliver over the next ten years or so, given good oil field practice and prudent concern for reserves; and the reliability of supply, which, apart from unexpectedly serious political disruptions that do not lend themselves to analysis, depends largely on the willingness and ability of the country to ensure the maintenance of supply in accordance with its potentialities.

Table 1 shows an impressionistic summary of the position of the seven countries considered here from these two points of view. The first two columns reflect reasonable estimates of the reserve position and near-future export potential, and serve primarily to rank the countries according to relative importance. I will not take time to discuss them, for the estimates are necessarily rough. The basis for the evaluations expressed in the remaining columns requires explanation and discussion.

TABLE 1

Some Factors Affecting Middle East Oil Exports

Country	(1) Reserve potential	(2) Export potential	(3)[b] Domestic financial needs in relation to revenues	(4)[b] International aspirations
Iran	●●●●●●	●●●●●●	●●●●●	●●●●●
Saudi Arabia	●●●●●●	●●●●●		
	●●●●●●	●●●●●●	●●	●●● (●?)
Iraq	●●● (●?)	●●● (●?)	●●● (●?)	●●
Kuwait	●●●●	●●●	●	●
Abu Dhabi	●●	●●	● (●?)	●
Libya	●●	●●	●[a]	● (●?)
Algeria	●	●	●●●●●	●

[a] Assuming no union with Egypt.
[b] In columns (3) and (4) the greater the number of blobs the more important the factor as a positive incentive to export.
Rows cannot be added to estimate total weight of country.

FINANCIAL NEEDS AND ABSORPTIVE CAPACITY

The relative weight given to the different countries in column (3) of Table 1 is intended to reflect the importance of each country's domestic requirements for revenues as an incentive to sell more oil. Thus a country whose revenues greatly exceed its ability to use them at home will be given a low weight. Domestic requirements are of great importance for Iran and Algeria. Both have ambitious programmes for domestic investment and can absorb large amounts of funds. In Algeria especially the oil industry will itself demand much investment. Iran has an expensive defence programme. Both can be expected to want to increase exports to the extent that reserves permit. Iraq will also want to spend a great deal domestically, but for somewhat different reasons. While the size of the population, the availability of resources and the opportunities for investment are all favourable for unusually rapid economic development and absorption of capital investment, political conditions still inhibit confident advance, especially in agriculture. The country has a development plan but in the past has rarely been able to spend the money allocated to it. Iraq's demands for revenues will not, therefore, arise so much from the needs of its general investment programme as from the desire to invest heavily in developing its own oil resources to meet a variety of political and military objectives, and to demonstrate that the particular direction its own oil policy has taken is profitable.

By contrast, the remaining four countries—Saudi Arabia, Kuwait, Abu Dhabi and Libya—have more funds than they can currently absorb, and they can expect a great deal more in the future. They will hardly feel a strong need for still more although they will, of course, continually press for more in the costless form of higher taxes and prices. If the projected union between Libya and Egypt is successfully completed, however, the financial needs of the two countries together will strain Libya's revenues and may cause a drastic revision in her approach towards oil exports, although her reserve position is not among the strongest.

Thus our countries can be divided into two groups with respect to the urgency of their demands for revenues: those which see opportunities for investment or other expenditures and will continually want more funds to take advantage of them, and those which are uncertain whether the investment opportunities open to them will be more profitable than the conservation of their oil for the future. They can also be divided into two groups with respect to the availability of reserves: those which fear a fall in the reserve/production ratio in the reasonably near future and those which are not as yet concerned with the problem. If we make a cross-classification, we have countries which (a) fear for their reserves and need funds urgently; (b) fear for their reserves but have no great need of more funds; (c) have ample reserves and need funds; and (d) have ample reserves and do not need more funds.

Only Algeria is in the first category. Exploration and development costs are rising significantly, her export surplus is not great and financial needs are high. She will be intensely concerned to raise the unit price of sales and will have every incentive to increase output as far as is prudent. In category (b) are Kuwait and Libya. Neither will press for greater revenues if these would cost very much. The fear for reserves implies that they consider oil output a cost. They will naturally press for higher unit revenues but their supply curves for oil may well be backward rising—after a point they may curve backwards, implying that greater revenues will call forth lower quantities. Both have already cut back output in spite of the fact that revenues obtained and invested today will yield a return while oil not produced today may fall in value later. For both countries, a calculation of the trade-off between the present and future would seem likely to support continued restriction of the rate at which current reserves are depleted.

In category (c)—ample reserves and a high perceived need for funds—are Iran and Iraq, and both countries can therefore be expected to be willing to increase supply, especially, perhaps, Iraq in view of her feeling of deprivation with respect to output over the past ten years and her reserve potential. In Iran reserves will probably give rise to some uneasiness much earlier than in Iraq.

Saudi Arabia is certainly in category (d)—ample reserves and excess funds —and perhaps Abu Dhabi. In Saudi Arabia reserves are expected to support rising rates of production well beyond a reasonable planning horizon, and thus a barrel produced today is generally assumed to be costless in terms of the use of resources. At the same time, a dollar earned and invested today can earn future revenues. In these conditions, it will not pay to restrict production. But there is another very important consideration.

It is possible that as oil revenues mount and with them investment outside the country either in the form of portfolio investment or of direct investment in productive projects, perhaps notably in downstream activities in the oil industry itself, objections to such investment, which are already of some importance in the Arab world, might become intensified. If it should seem that the revenues were benefiting either foreign companies or foreign countries more than the local people, considerable agitation against increasing oil exports could easily arise. The standard of living of the area is not high and there will be strong pressures for large sums to be spent on directly increasing consumption. To the extent that such expenditures are insufficient to satisfy the rising aspirations of people, for there is a genuine limit on how fast money can be spent, it is possible that the continued accumulation of revenues and their use abroad will come under increasing criticism and the demand to 'keep oil in the ground' may gain widespread support, especially among radical nationalist and anti-western (-capitalist) elements.

The argument that when reserves are so large that a barrel of oil not produced today has no present value, and that it therefore pays to produce if the revenues can earn a positive return after making allowance for varying degrees of risk, is not one that carries much conviction to those who think largely in political terms, especially when the world is ringing with cries of oil scarcity. For most ordinary people there is something intuitively wrong with the notion that it may not pay a country to wait even 30 years for a much higher yield than is obtainable today—and oil is also known as 'black gold' which, in the Middle East, implies that it should be hoarded! Certainly if foreign investment does not yield a reasonably high rate of return to the exporting countries, the force of these arguments will become even greater. Moreover, there is some fear that present international institutional arrangements are inadequate to absorb funds on the scale required, although adaptations to meet rising investment needs are already occurring—witness the growth of banks in which Arab groups have an interest. Others will undoubtedly come along, while the US government is particularly stressing the importance of creating outlets for surplus revenues.

It is difficult to judge how far these considerations can be expected to influence the willingness of countries with larger revenues than they can use to increase oil exports. But a number of countries, including Saudi Arabia, may have international aspirations which could in some degree offset the type of pressures just discussed.

INTERNATIONAL ASPIRATIONS

As can be seen from the fourth column of Table 1, all of the countries, except perhaps Libya at the present time, have some international incentive to maintain or increase oil exports apart from the simple economic one of earning the revenues they feel they need; nevertheless there is a more positive sign, so to speak, for some countries than for others. While it seems that Libya has aspirations to become a powerful leader in the Arab world, her hopes must rest more on her political appeal aided by the availability of liquid funds than on the strength of her economy. As noted above, a successful union with Egypt would dramatically strengthen the incentive to increase revenues from the sale of Libya's oil and would undoubtedly alter the weight of the present relative to the future in her calculations.

Algeria, Kuwait and Abu Dhabi are already on good terms with most countries of the world and seem to be largely influenced by commercial considerations. None of these has any particular international incentive to depart from straightforward economic behaviour with respect to oil. None of them would be reluctant to jeopardise its current international relationships by taking an active part in advocating the reduction of oil supplies for either political or bargaining purposes, although Kuwait and Abu Dhabi have little choice than to follow the lead of their more powerful neighbour.

On the other hand, Iran, Saudi Arabia, and Iraq have an incentive to go out of their way to strengthen their ties with the importing countries. The first two countries have declared their desire to invest downstream outside their own boundaries in order to build their own national oil companies into internationally integrated companies. The Shah seems to be grooming his country to take a leading role as an economically and politically great power in Asia, and thus an important power in the rest of the world. The growth of economic ties with Western industrial countries which are closer than those of trade and especially related to the country's one great resource, oil, seems to be an aspect of his vision. To achieve this he will have to draw not only on oil revenues but also on oil supplies, but it must be recognised that investment outside the country will be unlikely to absorb a significant part of the country's revenues in the foreseeable future.

Saudi Arabia does not have the resources of Iran and cannot develop into a great industrial country. But it could conceivably build Petromin into a strong internationally integrated oil company. It cannot do this without the co-operation of the importing countries. An ambition to do this could possibly help to offset unfavourable reaction to downstream investment outside the country.

Iraq has long suffered from its conflict with the companies and from a sense of isolation not only from the Western world, but also from the rest of the Arab world, largely because of its own political policies and behaviour. As a result it has turned increasingly to the countries of Eastern Europe and, predictably, is feeling restless under the restraints and problems that have accompanied these relationships. Now that Iraq has settled its quarrel with the oil companies, and for other reasons, it can be expected to be increasingly anxious to mend its fences with countries both within and outside the Arab world. It is likely to want to improve its relations with the consuming countries and with the oil companies, partly to diversify its sources of technology and skills, to widen its markets for oil, and to escape from the straitjacket of barter agreements.

Finally, there is the possibility that the exporting countries will deny oil, especially to US companies, as a means of bringing pressure on the US to change its wholehearted support of Israel. This seems to me highly improbable. No country has obtained much of a hearing for this kind of action (except for a short time after the Khartoum conference following the six-day war), but there are indications that exporting countries may in some ways favour their friends and be somewhat unwilling to expand output at high rates in order to meet the demands of countries supporting policies inimical to them. There is reason to think that these possibilities are already beginning to become more widely appreciated, especially in the United States. If in fact that country adopts a more even-handed attitude towards the conflict in the Middle East, the picture with respect to oil supplies will almost certainly be less gloomy.

From the point of view of the availability of oil from the Middle East to meet the rising demands of the industrialised world, the overall appraisal falling out of this analysis is by no means pessimistic, although prices can be expected to go as high as the importing countries will accept. Apart from the eruption of a generalised political conflict, the major caveat to be added relates to the possibility of confrontations in bargaining over taxes or buy-back prices, and the accompanying tactical mistakes if 'brinkmanship' is carried so far that little room is left for manoeuvre. Even then, however, the likelihood is simply that the remaining interests of the oil companies would be nationalised or some of their existing contractual obligations abrogated, and after all this has been the chief threat all along. Price negotiations then break down and the question is how far or under what conditions will this bring a disruption of the supplies of oil. This leads us to the question of the future of the international companies.

FUTURE OF THE INTERNATIONAL COMPANIES IN THE MIDDLE EAST

In my judgement the policies of the major oil-exporting countries point in only one direction: the elimination of the equity interest of the international oil companies in the major producing companies, and this within the decade. Others, however, hold that 'participation', or joint ventures with shared equity, will be the norm for the future. Algeria has long had joint ventures with its former concessionaires; participation agreements have been negotiated by the Gulf States; Libya was demanding them although she seems now to have changed her mind; Iraq is reportedly willing for a participation arrangement with the Basrah Petroleum Company. The Oil Minister of Saudi Arabia has hailed participation as the 'alternative to nationalisation' with great advantages for the participating governments. But how stable are such arrangements likely to be?

At the time when OPEC demanded participation and the companies would not hear of it, participation as an alternative to nationalisation did seem to have very strong arguments in its favour. Its achievement was quite rightly looked upon as a victory for the OPEC countries, and the companies only accepted it in the face of threats they evidently considered serious and credible. Nevertheless, one is inclined to think that as time and negotiations wore on the companies began to see advantages to themselves in the arrangements, so fast had events been moving in the oil world and so strong had the governments' position become. Now it seems likely that events have moved too fast even from the point of view of the governments of the Gulf and that the present participation agreements will soon seem as inappropriate as the Geneva agreements, signed little more than a year ago, now seem to them. What does participation now offer them that nationalisation would jeopardise?

Essentially the advantages are three: the government obtains control but need not pay for all the assets, and the companies provide equity capital; the technical, managerial and commercial expertise of the companies remains at the disposal of the joint ventures at no extra cost; and the exporting governments are not themselves required to sell through their state companies any more crude oil than they want to, the companies being required to take the balance on stipulated terms and subject to the tax arrangements the government imposes.

As we have seen, finance is likely to be a serious problem only for Iran, Algeria, and for a while, perhaps Iraq. Algeria seems uninterested in the problem now and can be left out of this discussion. Iran's latest move does not require the payment of compensation and she has evidently arranged to obtain finance from the companies in ways which apparently help to solve the problems of the United States companies respecting tax credits. In addition, compensation, which would follow the formula worked out for the participation agreements, is not great. Saudi Arabia, Kuwait, Abu Dhabi and, for the moment at least, Libya could easily afford the financial cost of nationalisation.

Iran has shown that the managerial, technical, and commercial expertise of the companies can be obtained on a contractual basis to the extent desired, including co-operation in downstream investments outside the country. Clearly the companies have every incentive to provide whatever help proves necessary to keep the oil flowing, and one would expect them to continue to carry out managerial and technical functions under contract to the governments.

And finally markets. With the companies as long-term offtakers why should the problem of marketing for the exporting countries be any different from what it is now? Zeki Yamani is probably correct in wanting to retain the companies as partners, largely because of the shield their marketing position provides against price erosion. But there are many who firmly believe that the OPEC countries, led in this respect by Saudi Arabia, could easily maintain a common front on prices even if they themselves were responsible for making the contracts with the companies and for selling as much as they desired directly to other users. Even Shaikh Yamani insists that if the governments were forced to nationalise, any short-term fall in prices that might follow would soon be righted and prices would then go higher than ever under pressure from an OPEC cartel. Clearly one cannot have it both ways: if OPEC could operate an effective price cartel, the only remaining argument for the governments in favour of participation as an alternative to nationalisation is not very convincing; if OPEC could not be expected to do so, then one must ask what are the advantages to the importing countries of supporting arrangements which seem to operate primarily as a device to keep up the cost of imported oil? The only reasonable answer, and the one given by Shaikh Yamani, is that such arrangements may help to integrate the exporting countries more closely into international markets and international relationships, and thus help to ensure the supply of oil on negotiated terms as contrasted to a possible free-for-all system where the most irresponsible could seriously upset the market. The test of this pudding will be in the eating.

From the point of view of the exporting countries, however, the question arises, given the historical legacy of attitudes towards the companies in the area, which have not been one whit softened by the vigorous attacks of the Shah and the statements of the oil minister of Saudi Arabia, can these two types of arrangements—participation on the one hand and nationalisation on the other—survive side by side in the Middle East so far as they apply to the major sources of oil?

The answer depends in the first instance on what happens in negotiations over tax prices, buy-back prices, etc.—and this will also be the crucial test for the companies. Here I am not entirely optimistic. The danger is great that the governments of the oil-exporting countries may push their demands further than the consuming countries are prepared to permit the companies to go, for they feel justified in asking for as much as they think the consuming countries can be made to pay, including the very large sums now being collected in excise taxes. They believe that it is reasonable and not 'unfair' to ask (at least of the rich countries—the poor countries may worry them a bit) the 'full value' of their oil, including the producer rent as well as the consumer surplus. To obtain this they may threaten too much, but threats have worked in the past, why should they not be expected to work as well in the future?

It may be that in the past the governments of importing countries, and in particular the United States government, encouraged the companies to accept the demands of the exporting countries. But balance of payments considerations and fears of adding oil to inflationary flames will certainly cause governments to refuse requests for higher prices at some point. One suspects that that point is very nearly reached, but in any case importers must stick somewhere and if nevertheless the exporting countries then insist on again raising taxes, the companies will have to resist. If negotiations have been accompanied by threats like those in the recent past, the exporting countries may have little room left for manoeuvre and may have to nationalise, whether they really want to or not. But as suggested above, they will very likely by that time have concluded that little if anything is lost by doing so, providing relations with the companies have not become too acrimonious.

Except for attempts to revise the Geneva agreements respecting the value of currencies, negotiations over tax prices should not again take place until after 1975. If at that point nationalisation does occur, as I expect it to, the issues will no longer relate to negotiations over tax rates or buy-back prices; rather the national oil companies of the Middle East will be negotiating actual crude oil sales to the companies and to others in the markets of the world. There is no reason to think that an OPEC price cartel, which would be attempted, could push prices any higher than could the governments under participation arrangements and there is some reason to think it would not be so effective. This brings us to the role of OPEC.

THE ROLE OF OPEC

OPEC has been and still is, a valuable asset for the oil-exporting countries. It has brought them some sense of unity of purpose, has built up expertise and knowledge among them, and has enabled them to present an effective common front to the companies on many matters. This was especially important during the 1960s when a variety of genuine anomalies in the concession agreements were being dealt with.

But now in the 1970s the situation has changed. There is little evidence that the collective bargaining power which OPEC represents was important in those crucial Libyan negotiations in 1970. Nor was OPEC pressure needed to enable Iran and Saudi Arabia, acting together and with Saudi Arabia representing the Gulf States, to bring about the Teheran price agreement which was inevitably followed by the Tripoli agreement. The real power now lies elsewhere than in OPEC.

OPEC cannot bring effective pressure to attain any objectives which are not supported by these two countries to achieve their own ends. The role of OPEC is now primarily that of a useful secretariat, an organiser of meetings in which issues can be debated and feelings expressed, a forum in which agreement can be obtained on the appointment of negotiators, and a supporting background chorus for the leading countries. It seems unlikely that, even with the support of such members, it could operate an effective price cartel. To make such a cartel stick it would be necessary to ensure that those countries in our category (c), having ample reserves and a strong need of funds, do not take advantage of the situation to raise their revenues by selling a little more in defiance of price agreements, and this category includes two of the most well-endowed countries in the area—Iran and Iraq.

However, in this context most people are not really talking about a cartel at all. The argument that the OPEC countries could effectively control prices even if each of them were responsible for its own marketing, really rests on the belief that Saudi Arabia could call the tune and the others, being few, would surely follow. It is believed that the reserves of the area are so concentrated in Saudi Arabia that if she were prepared to refuse to sell except to those who paid her price, this alone would be sufficient to extract the price. If some others decided to sell for less, the amount they could sell would be so small in comparison with that of Saudi Arabia (with the presumption that Iran would follow) that it would make little difference and could be ignored, just as a big company can ignore the chiselling of a small one. This situation is not a cartel, of course, but a monopoly with a fringe of followers.

Such a situation would be highly unstable if the importing countries were prepared to bargain seriously and to refuse excessive prices. Iran, and even Iraq, might well find it not only inconvenient to hold back supplies but also inconsistent with their international aspirations, as suggested earlier. If they do not easily follow the lead of Saudi Arabia, then prices would soften, or at least not rise further. OPEC might be able to co-ordinate policies a little, and companies and consuming countries might not press very hard on prices for reasons of their own. In particular, company costs of developing output elsewhere are still very high and the United States drive to establish new and adequate domestic supplies of energy will be expensive. Hence, great efforts to press import costs down very far will probably not be made.

There is little point in carrying this kind of speculation further here. In brief, I would expect participation agreements to break down before very long and the governments of the exporting countries to follow the lead of Iran and take over their own industry. Such a change need not lead to a crisis of relations with the producing countries, although it may do so; it would seem more likely that negotiated arrangements to retain the technical and other services of the companies would be made. Some mild competition may be introduced into the market for crude oil. In the meantime, we may expect continued further investment by some of the producing countries in downstream activities outside their own countries and, with luck, some reasonably satisfactory relationships developing.

Discussion

Mr John W. Peters (Esso Petroleum Co. Ltd): The picture you have painted is of the major Middle East producers (perhaps the Seven Big Brothers?) holding most of the cards when it comes to future price negotiations. Do you think there is a chance that by late 1974 or 1975, when renegotiation of the Teheran Agreement is due, there may be a swing of the supply pendulum which will temporarily offset this advantage? This could happen for example if producers throughout the world pull out all the stops to meet the current short term problems, if there is some easing of tension with Israel and if there is a warm winter which holds down demand.

Professor Penrose: I do not think so. Why should the Saudis increase output any more than is necessary to optimise their position? Even if all these soothing, happy events that you mention take place, there is still the commercial aspect of the matter. It does not necessarily pay the producing countries to exhaust their resources as rapidly as we might want. It does pay countries to take advantage of their monopoly position. The oil companies did this for a long time and their position weakened because they got into competition. I do not see this happening within the next few years. It is possible, if participation breaks down and the governments start selling their own oil. This might ease the pressure on prices, but I cannot go as far as Professor Adelman does in thinking that this will lead to the re-emergence of surplus. I do not see why we should accept any other assumption than that we are faced with the kind of squeeze that will occur when people have control of an important resource and are taking advantage of it. This is not necessarily a crisis, although some people may expect a 'confrontation'.

Professor P. R. Odell (Erasmus University, Rotterdam): The speaker has previously argued the case of the majors' ability to control surplus out of the Middle East. This was lost by virtue of competitive pressures in the 1960s—but has now been regained out of the collusion of the oil producing countries so producing a unity of interests between the parties—to the detriment of the consuming countries, developed and developing. In light of this, is the creation of 'uncertainty' about the future level of demand for oil adequate to prevent that rise of market prices (beyond the rise of government tax take per brl) that the speaker confidently expected—and did not see as likely to give rise to any serious problem? Would the speaker thus comment on:

(a) the apparent collusion between producing countries and the international oil companies arising out of this common interest;

(b) the validity of a policy by consuming countries to maximise the certainty that future demand for imported oil will not measure up to the expectations of exporting countries and oil companies;

(c) the hypothesis of Adelman that maximising demand (US & W. Europe & Japan etc.) will cause one or more parties in the 'cartel' to break the oligopolistic position and lead to reduced prices for oil more in line with the long run supply price of Middle East crude?

Professor Penrose: What are the consuming countries going to do?—get together, and have a confrontation? This might have been possible at one point in the past, but not now. I don't see the United States controlling its own independents, let alone the Japanese and the Europeans. What needs to be done is to find some way of limiting all the little groups competing for their little bits and pieces of oil all over the place because this is pushing up the free-market price at the present time, but I do not think the consumers are in a good position. Moreover, I think it is misleading to use such words as collusion in all this. You know the oil companies have been called the 'business in between' by Jack Hartshorn and they like to put this image over but they can do little now. Governments have now more or less taken over on both sides of the fence. Whether the oil companies have the same interests as producing countries depends entirely on their power to raise the prices of products and this is now no longer entirely under their control. Moreover, on my scenario they will soon be pushed out of the producing end as owners and will be interested in their fees for working as agents or contractors of the producing countries. Now, with respect to Adelman's proposition, this does pre-suppose that there is a cartel, and that what you do is to tempt people to break the cartel. His arguments with respect to what happened earlier with rising demand providing an incentive for oil companies to cut prices in some way or other are sound because they did not really have a cartel. Even then there was need to compete. Now we don't need to rely on a cartel. People who think that the problem arises because of an OPEC cartel which will tend to break, seem to me to be slightly on the wrong track because of the importance of one country, Saudi Arabia, where reserves are being increasingly concentrated. Later, competition might arise as Iraq's reserves get more established. This just might be the country where the softening of prices will begin to occur towards the end of the 80s. This is just a possibility.

Mr C. M. Dalley (Iraq Petroleum Co. Ltd): Your paper has emphasised the different role of the international oil companies. These companies have demonstrated that oil reserves have been identified as sufficient to meet the demands up to 1985. They have also demonstrated that they can agree with exporting countries on the form of producing organisations. There is thus no problem left which is within the scope of the oil companies. The present so called crisis is nothing but a hiccup in the supply/demand balance. Do you agree that what is required is a reasonable degree of co-ordination between consuming countries—and I mean their governments—about supplies which, after agreement, can then be implemented by the oil industry?

Professor Penrose: Of course we want to have a rational distribution of resources, but whose rationality are we concerned with? The argument that the oil companies (which you call the oil industry) have put forward for so long—that we have no conflicts, that our objectives are the same—is just not true. There are enormous conflicts of interest, and the oil companies still have enormous power, but not the kind I think that Professor Adelman is talking about. They have the power that comes from the expertise they've got, they're the only ones that can do some of the jobs that need to be done, and that is why the exporting countries will take them, the importing countries will take them, the governments are going to want them around, whether or not they nationalise the companies.

CHAPTER 13

Oil in the US Energy Crisis—Problems and Prospects

JOHN H. LICHTBLAU

Executive Director, Petroleum Industry Research Foundation Inc., New York, USA

It is difficult to imagine an industry more characterised by internal contradictions, inconsistencies and radical reversals than the oil industry. The fact that I have been invited to Europe to report on the American oil shortage is a good example of this.

The US is still the world's largest oil producer—its current total output of 11 mbd of crude oil and natural gas liquids is almost equal to the combined production of Saudi Arabia and Iran. Our dependence on foreign oil is currently only 35%, compared to Europe's and Japan's 90% plus; and since the beginning of this year we have had virtually no restriction on the importation of crude oil and refined products. Yet, while Europeans are merrily preparing for their summer vacation drives, Americans are told they may have to stay home for lack of gasoline. And this in the country which measures standard of living by gasoline consumption per head and has opted against mass transit because it would mean less driving.

IS THE OIL SHORTAGE REAL?

I would like to discuss some of the reasons underlying this situation because it has a direct bearing on the European situation. But before doing so I would like to address myself briefly to the question of whether there really is an oil-products shortage in the US. As you may know, neither the press nor the public are convinced that the shortage is real. And, in the halls of Congress, charges that it is 'contrived' by the major oil companies to raise the prices and/or to drive out the independent marketers are frequently heard.

The shortage will bring about higher prices and it will be especially hard on the independents. Nevertheless, it is real and not rigged. On the other hand, it is likely to be relatively small, at least for the remainder of this year. At present our refineries, working virtually at peak production, process about 3 000 000 bd less gasoline than our calculated demand. Some of the deficit is being made up by imports from Puerto Rico and the Virgin Islands (a regular source of gasoline imports) and some can be made up by drawing our stocks down. But about 150 000 bd of the deficit must come from overseas sources over the next four to five months. This volume represents 2–3 % of total demand, which is the extent of our potential gasoline shortage. As of this moment the shortage has not reached the end user. But he will probably, though not certainly, feel it during the peak driving months of July and August because we are unlikely to import the entire amount required.

The importance of the deficit, however, lies not so much in its size but in the fact that for the first time in history US refineries are unable to meet the normal gasoline requirements of the American public. How did we get there? Certainly not unavoidably, nor unforeseeably.

WHY IS THERE A REFINING SHORTAGE?

There was nothing more obvious than the fact that if we stopped building new refining capacity while our demand continued to grow, we would eventually run short of domestically refined products. Government agencies and industry forecasts have predicted the current situation for at least the past 2½ years. In the past two years US refining capacity rose by only 670 000 bd and 160 000 bd respectively compared with 1 400 000 bd and 1 260 000 bd in Europe whose demand is of the same general magnitude as ours, and current US capacity (end of May) is virtually unchanged from that of the beginning of the year. There are four reasons for this development.

The first and most important reason is not man-made but the consequence of a natural resource shortage. US refineries have traditionally been built primarily as outlets for US crude oil, mostly by companies with controlled crude oil production. As production increased refining capacity was expanded accordingly. However, US crude oil production reached its peak in 1970 and has been declining since. Thus, for the last three years it would have made no sense to build new refineries to run on domestic crude oil.

The reason why the increase in crude oil imports which offset the decline in domestic production did not generate new refining capacity is, in large part, the lack of government policy. Our mandatory oil import programme was reasonably stable throughout most of the 1960s. But from 1969 until May, 1973, the programme was administered on an unpredictable *ad hoc* basis with each decision increasing the degree of uncertainty. It was just as possible to detect signs that the government was going to opt for a highly protective policy on crude oil imports as that a major import liberalisation was planned. There were clear indications that more product imports were to be permitted and official statements condemning the exportation of refining capacity by means of additional refined product imports.

Small wonder that few companies were willing to spend several hundred million dollars to build a new refinery under these circumstances, particularly for the past two years when everyone was impatiently waiting for the long-promised new government oil import policy. It is interesting that within one month after the announcement of the new policy several major domestic refining capacity expansions were announced.

The few companies that did want to take a chance during that interim period and build refineries on the East Coast to process imported crude oil ran into fierce environmental opposition wherever they tried to locate. Had this opposition, which is mainly of a local character, not existed some 500 000 bd of additional refining capacity would have been completed or under construction at this time—enough to have averted the current shortage.

Finally, there is the problem of excess refining capacity which has plagued the industry throughout the 1960s. This cannot be laid at the door of anyone else but is strictly a reflection of market competition. It has brought about the famous 'incremental barrel' which became the life blood of the independent marketers, particularly in the case of gasoline, but turned into a Frankensteinian monster for the refiners who had created it to enhance their profits. Instead, it came to have just the opposite effect, so that from 1952 to 1972 tank wagon gasoline prices increased by less than 15% while the general wholesale price index rose by 58%. Under these conditions, there was, understandably, not too much interest in building additional refining capacity. This, too, had an impact on the current situation.

THE IMPACT OF THE NEW GOVERNMENT POLICY

Having enumerated all the reasons for the existing refining shortage, the fact remains that it is a man-made shortage and can be removed by the simple expedient of building additional refining capacity at a faster rate than the growth in consumption. This is precisely what can be expected now that the government, very belatedly, has enunciated its new import policy. The policy permits the unlimited importation of crude oil against payment of a modest import fee; it gives a special incentive to build new refineries or expand existing ones by waiving the fee on the bulk of their crude oil imports for a limited period and by putting a fairly high import fee on all finished oil products.

The combination of these two devices should give domestic refineries a competitive edge over foreign ones which would be further strengthened by the establishment of superports on the US East and Gulf Coasts. The President's energy message proposes national legislation to build such ports in US offshore areas.

That does not mean we are out of the woods. On the contrary, for the next 2½ years at least, our deficit in light and middle distillates will increase. By 1975, we are likely to require 475 000–575 000 bd of gasoline imports and 600 000 bd of middle distillate imports. By comparison, in 1972 our imports of these two products amounted to 70 000 and 180 000 bd respectively.

US IMPORTS AND EUROPEAN PRICES

A good part of the increased imports will come from the Caribbean and eastern Canada where additional refining capacity of about 1 mbd is scheduled to come on stream between now and the end of 1975. But part of our requirements will undoubtedly have to be met from Europe. To this extent our situation will affect European supplies and prices.

I would like to digress here for a moment to point out that whatever the reason for the current exceptionally high prices of refined oil products in European export markets, actual current US purchases are not the reason for it. Since the beginning of April, US gasoline imports from Europe averaged well under 10 000 bd while gas oil imports were equal to less than 1% of the European demand for this product. Obviously, these volumes are not sufficient to account for the 250% increase in gasoline prices nor the 150% increase in gas oil prices, relative to a year ago. But the expectation of higher US purchases is likely to have played a part in the increase. But here we get into the grey area where psychology and economics overlap.

Theoretically, our shortage of domestic gasoline and middle distillates should start to ease up after 1975 and could be over by the end of 1978. Whether this target can actually be reached will depend to some extent on the effectiveness of environmental opposition to new refineries and superports. If this opposition succeeds in blocking many such projects we will have no choice but to continue to export our refining capacity—probably to eastern Canada and the Caribbean. But the federal government and the oil industry are opposed to such a development.

THE OUTLOOK FOR DOMESTIC CRUDE OIL SUPPLIES

Now let us turn to the non-man-made aspect of the US energy shortage, that of our domestic crude oil supply. Here we are coming up against the inexorable finiteness of a non-renewable natural resource which after 122 years of commercial exploitation during which over 100 billion (10^9) brl were withdrawn is beginning to show signs of exhaustion. I think we can consider this an irreversible process. According to the National Petroleum Council's recent major study on the US Energy Outlook, the highest increase in crude oil production that can realistically be expected between 1970 and 1985 is in the order of 2 mbd. This is just about equal to the known potential productive capacity of the Alaskan North Slope. In other words, at best we will be able to maintain our existing productive capacity at its present level, with all increases in oil demand coming from abroad or from as yet undeveloped synthetic domestic sources. If we consider that by the beginning of this year 54% of the generally assumed total of 810 billion brl of original ultimately discoverable oil has already been found and that our cumulative historic recovery ratio is not quite one third of any oil discovered, such a development is not surprising. The remaining 46% of our ultimate oil resource will be far more difficult to discover and part of it is likely to elude us permanently because of inaccessibility or prohibitive cost.

Parenthetically, the situation is different for domestic natural gas. Only one third of ultimately discoverable gas reserves have been found and our offshore areas appear to hold much greater promise for major gas finds than oil finds. Thus, gas production, given sufficient economic incentives, will continue to rise, although for the remainder of this decade not at the rate of potential demand.

US AND FOREIGN PRICES

Price increases will of course help to maintain the production level of oil because it will permit us to engage in more secondary and tertiary recovery methods. But the price mechanism will not turn domestic production once again into a growth industry.

Nevertheless, substantial price increases in domestic oil can be expected. But they will not be the result of domestic political decisions nor free market conditions but of actions taken by the OPEC countries. By removing the import quota system and replacing it with a modest import fee the government has tied US prices directly to world prices. Considering the total rejection by the industry and the President of a much more modest proposal in the same direction advanced three years ago by the Cabinet Task Force on Oil Imports, the new policy may be considered a classic example of an 'agonising reappraisal'.

Thus, from now on OPEC will hold its benevolent price umbrella as firmly over the producers in Texas and Louisiana as it does over the British North Sea and the people of Norway. It is getting difficult to tell who wins and who loses in this game.

As a result of the new US policy, the point of competition between foreign and domestic oil has moved from the US East Coast to the Gulf Coast. At the East Coast foreign oil from all major supply sources now has a net competitive advantage over domestic oil at the import fee of 21c/brl. East Coast refineries will therefore run entirely on foreign crude oil in the future, unless domestic crude oil is discovered off the Atlantic Coast.

DEVELOPING ALTERNATIVE US RESOURCES

Tying domestic oil to the rising level of world oil prices has wider implications than boosting US prices. It will speed up the development of shale oil production and coal liquefaction. Both these processes are considered feasible from the technological as well as the engineering point of view. However, economically they are not yet fully justified, although they are not far from it. The kind of world price increases generally projected over the next five to eight years would certainly make them competitive. That does not give us a short-term alternative to increased imports at rising prices, for there is no way of producing shale oil or liquefied coal in nationally significant quantities until after 1985. But the potential of these resources with their immense untapped reserves puts a time limit and an eventual price ceiling on our growing foreign oil requirements. To the extent to which the volume of our imports and the price we are willing to pay for it affect oil imports and prices everywhere, the potential availability of US synthetic oil on a massive scale is of global significance, provided we develop it forthwith.

In the meantime the US will have to act a bit like other oil importing nations. We will have to develop emergency storage facilities, we will have to adopt a stand-by plan to cope with interruption of imports and we will have to co-operate with other importing nations in whatever common policy can be agreed on. We will also have to learn not to panic at the balance of payments aspect of importing 8 to 10 mbd by 1980. The figure of $25 billion ($10^9$) frequently cited in this connection to call attention to the magnitude of the problem represents only the gross import cost. A significant part of this dollar outflow—perhaps as much as half—can be expected to be returned to the US in the form of additional exports, the inflow of foreign capital from the producing countries and the repatriation of US foreign oil company earnings. Thus, while the impact of our increased imports on the balance of payments is a legitimate object of concern, it is not an insurmountable problem, although right now when the gold sells in the London Market for $123 an ounce it may seem insurmountable.

In the final analysis we must remember that even 10 years from now the US will probably still be able to rely for about 55% of its oil requirements and about 77% of its total energy requirements on domestic and other secure North American sources. Compared to the oil and energy self-sufficiency ratios of most other major industrial nations, this does not appear excessive, provided we develop the safeguards and alternatives I have outlined.

Discussion

Miss M. P. Doyle (Esso Petroleum Co. Ltd): Is the Western Hemisphere aware of the problem the US 'solution' to its short-term product shortage might create for European refineries in view of the yield pattern in Europe producing so much fuel oil? Also does the US appreciate the possibility that increased crude imports might draw sweet crudes away from Europe and thus magnify the problem?'

Mr J. H. Lichtblau: Things are rough all over. Our East Coast refineries are designed to run on sour crude oil. Our Gulf Coast refineries are designed to run primarily on sweet domestic crude oil which is no longer available in sufficient quantities. They have to go and look in the market for sweet crude oil from Africa. Our East Coast refineries have always run primarily on Venezuelan crude oil which is sour. As far as our purchasing finished oil products like gasoline from Europe is concerned, of course we do not expect to fill all the 2% gasoline shortage from Europe. As I said, a large part of it can come in from Puerto Rico, the Virgin Islands and drawing on our stocks. Our traditional import sources are in the Caribbean and we will continue to bring in gasoline from there. But eventually we may be looking in Europe for as much as 100 000–150 000 barrels a day. This is not happening now. Our present gasoline imports from Europe are very small, simply because they are not available. But if you look ahead to the next couple of years we will have to go to Europe for a fairly substantial amount of gasoline. If we do not get it we will have to have some kind of gasoline ration system in the United States. I do not expect imports ever to come to more than 5% of US demand. We have some flexibility in the United States. We can increase our gasoline yield at the expense of our distillate heating oil yields. There is a good reason for doing this because there is much more gas oil available in foreign markets than there is gasoline. The gasoline yield in Europe is about 15% while the gas oil yield is well over 30% so that the volume of gas oil available might be bigger. For that reason US refineries might maximise their gasoline yield domestically and concentrate more on importing middle distillates, but there is a problem even though there is excess refining capacity in Europe. At the same time you are quite correct to stress the fact that if you produce more heavy fuel oil and have no outlet for it, the market price will drop and of course refineries do not want this. They have had it in the past and the fuel oil price was extremely low for many years for that very reason. European refineries could produce additional amounts of residual fuel oil if there were some outlet. We may have to let up on our fuel oil sulphur restrictions in the United States. This would help greatly. Some industries have advocated this, but there is opposition from the environmentalists including government officials.

CHAPTER 14

Outlook for Europe

ADRIAN HAMILTON

The Financial Times

There may or may not be room for argument about whether the world actually faces an 'energy crisis' or not, but there can be little doubt that the experience of fuel supplies in the last few years has radically altered the way that consuming governments are now approaching the problem. Quite suddenly, the major fuel importing countries of the industrialised world have been forced to come face to face with some disturbing facts about their dependence on oil and the lack of flexibility that has grown up in energy patterns. Security of supply has rapidly replaced cost of fuels as the major source of concern among government planners. From defence of coal, economic ministries have moved to thoughts of how to expand solid fuel production. From relative passivity as regards the conduct of oil trade negotiations with the producing countries, the consuming states are now wondering how they can intervene more directly to protect their interests.

The problems of energy are in a sense common to virtually every industrialised country, but it is in Europe that they have perhaps been felt most sharply and most unsettlingly. The US situation may have developed more dramatically and the Japanese may have found themselves more vulnerable to changes outside their control, but it is the Europeans who seem to have been least prepared for the changes in the energy market augured by the oil industry-OPEC confrontations of the last few years and who seem most uncertain as to how to effect new policies to deal with the problems of the future.

INDUSTRIAL EXPANSION IN THE 1960s

The reasons for the near-neurotic deliberations now going on in European government circles are not hard to find. The tremendous industrial expansion of western Europe in the late fifties and sixties was fuelled very largely by abundant and cheap supplies of oil from the Middle East and North Africa. At a speed and to an extent which few people fully appreciated, imported oil took over from coal as the central source of primary energy for most of Western Europe and particularly for the fast growing European Economic Community.

Where indigenous coal formed by far the highest proportion of energy consumption in most European countries in the years after the war, by the beginning of the seventies its share of primary energy had fallen to 46% in the UK and 26·5% in Western Germany (35% with lignite). Production in France during the 15-year period, 1956–1971, was down 40%; Belgian output fell by over 60% and Dutch production was well on the way to being phased out altogether.

In OECD Europe as a whole, coal's share of total primary energy consumption fell from over 61% in 1960 to 29·4% in 1970 with a loss in actual volume of nearly 70 m tons of oil equivalent. Oil use, in the same period, shot up from 199·3 m tons of oil equivalent, or 32·6% of the total, in 1960, to 620·2 m tons of oil equivalent, or 59·5% of the total, in 1970.

During this time, despite various attempts by the EEC to formulate an overall energy policy, much of the thinking of consumer governments in Europe was directed towards trying to ensure that the decline in coal was rendered as painless as possible in terms of social effects through the use of direct subsidies and indirect aid in the form of fuel oil taxation, especially in the major coal producing countries of the UK and Germany.

On the oil side, perhaps the most effective action was taken in the market place. Both France and Italy and, to a lesser extent, Germany adopted policies of ensuring that at least a proportion of market sales were kept in the hands of national and state oil companies, with a reasonable degree of success. Efforts to promote active control of oil imports were much less successful.

Only France consistently argued for a 'dirigiste' policy towards crude oil sources from an early stage and equally consistently failed to get its views accepted by other members of the EEC, while its own policy on this score eventually fell foul of the Franco-Algerian debacle of 1971. Other countries, and in particular Germany and Italy, preferred a policy of free imports while at the same time attempting to ensure that their national oil companies gained an increasing control of crude oil sources through exploration and through deals with producer countries. None has achieved as much success in this course as might have been hoped. Exploration failures, the difficulties of competing with the great volumes of low-cost crude oil from the traditional Middle East concessions and lack of sufficient State financial support for companies (as witnessed most recently in the Deminex-BP negotiations on offshore Abu Dhabi) have all contributed to rather marginal development of the new state or national oil companies outside their own countries.

At the end of the day, too, there was never the incentive to go all out for state intervention in oil supplies. As long as oil was in plentiful supply and consistently falling in price, the French policies of planned investment and control of sources seemed both expensive and unnecessary to other countries. Energy, for too many consumers, could be taken for granted, and, in this atmosphere, the effort to produce overall energy policies tended to be limited to bureaucrats rather than politicians—a tendency that was strengthened by the failures of the UK fuel policy document of 1967.

THE END OF A BUYERS' MARKET

This complacency has been rudely shattered by the supply difficulties of 1970/1 and the OPEC price and participation negotiations since then. In retrospect, it would be easy to argue that the supply problems of the time and the apparent switch from a buyers' to a sellers' market in oil during the last few years has been exaggerated. But, however real the actual worries were, the implications of the developments were upsetting enough. Faced with a potential shortage of oil, Western Europe was made to realise how little flexibility there was in its energy system, and how far it was from achieving real flexibility in a four-fuel economy. Coal had declined to a point where resurgence was extremely difficult if not impossible in the short term. Nuclear power programmes were well behind schedule. Gas supplies were fully committed.

Oil, which had so long been relied onto fill the gap, was shown to be extremely vulnerable to concerted action by the major Middle East producers. The oil companies were too dependent on the profits and supplies of their major Middle East concessions to provide a real buffer between the producer and the consumer.

Looking to the future, Europe seemed faced with the rather gloomy prospect of increasing reliance on imported oil in a world in which the major industrialised nations would be competing more and more for available increments in supply from the central producing areas of the Middle East. The potential consequences for prices and Europe's import bill could be staggering enough with estimates suggesting that the deficit in trade on energy could be as high as $35 000 million in the mid-eighties, about half the figure concentrated on Germany and France. Added to this was the real fear that, in a tight supply situation, Europe might well be outbid for supplies by the richer forces of Japan and the US.

How far European governments, either separately or together, can take action to relieve this dependence on imported oil is the central question now facing officials and politicians. The answers are by no means clear. Much of the talk about possible shortages of oil remains highly speculative and there is much in the general energy situation which could be radically changed by new discoveries of oil or gas or technical breakthroughs in either the use or supply of fuels. If the last few years have proved anything in the energy sector, it has been just how vulnerable and imprecise forward estimates of supply and demand are, and it is hardly a field, therefore, which a mere journalist would tread with any confidence.

FUTURE ENERGY DEMAND IN EUROPE

On the demand side, of course, there remains an argument that supply/demand must, by their nature, even out and if supplies are not readily available then demand itself will tend to flatten out. This is hardly an argument that is likely to appeal to consumer governments anxious for growth and increasingly conscious of the dependence of industrial expansion on readily available supplies of fuel. Nevertheless, price is bound to influence both the rate of increase in demand and to induce consumers to look again at the efficiency with which they use energy.

The current inflation in all fuel prices will almost certainly restrict the degree to which consumers move to luxury uses of energy, like heating snow-ridden pavements in cities. Over the longer term it is likely to encourage the use of total energy schemes and more concentration on heat conserving materials and methods of construction in building, while the use of energy may well become an object of increasing attention by governments themselves which could well intervene to promote more efficient use by legislation or tax discrimination in car manufacture and power generation. Given current expectations of price it is very difficult to foresee European consumption of energy per head approaching anything like that now prevalent in the US, especially in the use of electricity.

Nevertheless, it seems unlikely that demand growth in Western Europe will veer dramatically from historic trends over the future. The effects of increased efficiency in fuel use will probably be more than compensated for by the effects of pollution legislation such as control of lead content in gasoline raising demand for fuel. Nor will price necessarily have the impact on energy use that some might hope. The marginal pricing which has been so strong a feature of the oil industry over the last decade still continues and, while the prices of oil and other fuels are almost certain to rise in real terms, the increases may well prove insufficient to overcome the problems of capital cost involved in greater efficiency in fuel use, while governments themselves, despite their policies towards energy, are liable to intervene to prevent too sharp a rise in fuel costs at any one time.

In the absence of a world recession, therefore, the growth in European energy demand seems likely to continue at a rate of around 5 to 5·5% through the rest of this decade and a rate of around 5% during the next decade, resulting in a primary energy demand of around 35 mbdoe by the end of the decade and over 45 mbdoe in 1985, including wastage, use of fuel in refineries, etc.

The pattern of fuels, on the other hand, will probably change direction somewhat from the past ten years and it is on this that consumer governments are now concentrating their attention. Of fundamental importance is the likely position of coal in long-term supplies. It has been the decline of coal that has caused the major problem of the past and it is its future which still casts the most uncertain shadow over the future.

COAL PRODUCTION

While the logical potential of coal production and the extent of indigenous reserves in Europe are encouraging, its economics are still far from buoyant. Much of the coal is deep mined and heavily labour intensive. Its real cost, if subsidies were fully included, would probably be in excess of a dollar per million Btu with little sign that its rate of price inflation will progressively reduce the margin between it and fuel oil.

Governments will almost certainly take action now to help their national coal industries with financial aid, as the UK is now doing, and the EEC as a whole seems likely to open the Community up to more imports of low-sulphur coal from Australia and the US. But the possibilities of radically improving coal prospects in the future European energy pattern still seem remote. The Dutch are now planning the closure of their last mine. The German coal industry, despite the increases in subventions, is now estimated to reduce production by at least 10 million tons a year and possibly 20 million tons by the middle of the decade with the closure of exhausted or uneconomic pits. France may well see a fall by 8 million tons in output over the next few years while Belgian production is expected to fall by nearly a third in the same period to between 10 and 11 million tons a year.

There remains the social problem of attracting new generations of miners to work deep-mined pits. Even in the UK, one retains a suspicion that recruitment to the mines is closely related to the level of unemployment. Most important of all, there is the problem of markets. In the industrial and domestic sectors, coal is losing its place almost irreversibly on grounds not only of cost but of handling and distribution. Steel continues to prove a buoyant market—although Europe is short of the grades of coal necessary to meet the demand—and the electricity generating industry in almost every country is now anxious to diversify away from coal towards gas, oil and nuclear power.

On all these grounds it would seem safest to predict that coal will at best preserve its place in the energy picture on volume grounds while losing its proportional contribution to the whole. At worst, it could still decline a good way further. In very rough figures, therefore, one might expect to see coal output falling to perhaps around 4–4·5 mbdoe in Western Europe by the end of the decade, and possibly holding this level through the eighties.

NUCLEAR POWER

Nuclear power, on the other hand, undoubtedly continues to hold great promise over the longer term future, although here it is the problem of lead time that more than anything else limits its contribution over the next ten years. The 'energy crisis' of the last few years has caught Europe badly off-balance in this sector. Only the UK has a strongly developed nuclear power programme—not without its own problems—and there has been nothing like the massive order of new nuclear stations on this side of the Atlantic which has so marked the US in the late sixties.

Recent estimates suggest that by 1980 installed nuclear capacity may have leapt to some 95·3 million kilowatts in Western Europe as a whole (over half of it in Germany and the UK) although, with slippages, there is room to doubt whether this figure will be achieved. By 1985, however, the total should have doubled again and be contributing over 8 % of Western European energy consumption, with a continuous progression after that at even faster rates.

NATURAL GAS

In the meantime, it will probably be natural gas that shows the fastest rate of growth and achieves the greatest contribution to taking up the increment in European energy demand over the next ten years or so. Although recent re-assessments of the Groningen onshore gas field in Holland have substantially reduced the field's expected output, production is still rising fast, a major portion of it for export. The North Sea is already contributing about 2500 to 3000 mcfd. By 1975, its output should have risen to nearer 5000 mcfd while, by 1980, my own guess would be that production from all sectors of the North Sea should total at least 10 000 mcfd and possibly nearer 12 000 mcfd.

Added to this, Europe has already contracted to take very substantial amounts of Russian and North African gas over the coming decades. Contracts for the import of Russian natural gas already amount to about 2000 mcfd and it would be surprising if this was not increased. Deals to import Algerian gas involve nearly the same amount, while Libyan imports are expected to reach about 500 mcfd by the middle of the decade.

During this decade, Western European use of gas is expected to more than triple from around 8000 to nearer 27–30 000 mcfd, of which some 15 to 20 % may be imported. Gas's overall contribution to Western Europe's energy picture, as a result, should rise from nearly 8 % at present to around 14 % by 1980 and perhaps nearer 18 % by 1985.

OIL SUPPLIES

Even assuming the higher forecasts for all these fuels, however, it will still be to oil that Western Europe will have to look to meet the great bulk of its energy demand over the foreseeable future. Against some 15 mbd at present, consumption in the area is expected to rise to around 22·5 mbd by 1980 and nearer 30 mbd by 1985, or nearly 65 % of the area's total primary energy requirements.

North Sea oil, of course, will do something to take up this increment in demand. Estimates vary widely and exploration of the northern waters is still not sufficiently mature to predict likely reserves and production with any certainty. But I think it would be surprising if the areas offshore North Western Europe did not produce at least 5 mbd and probably nearer 7 mbd in the mid-eighties. The problem will be the pace at which development is carried out and here I believe that nationalistic politics will intervene to reduce the pace of exploration and exploitation.

This still means a substantial growth in oil import requirements to about 19–20 mbd in 1980 and over 20 mbd in 1985—at a time when the other major industrial areas of the world, including Eastern Europe, will be upping their import volumes by even greater amounts and looking to the very same sources as Europe for the basic source of their supplies.

THE ROLE OF RUSSIA

Russia may provide some flexibility as to crude oil sources, although its determination to open up its considerable reserves in the eastern areas with western help would seem to favour the US and Japanese markets rather than those of Western Europe. Recent trends also suggest that exports to Western Europe are being achieved at the expense of imports into Eastern Europe from the Middle East and one is left with the strong suspicion that hopes that Russia may provide the *deus ex machina* of the world's oil problems are based on a fundamental misunderstanding of the degree to which Russian politics are moving towards a genuine detente with the outside world and the degree to which the Soviet leadership is prepared to allow western capital and technology to take a hold of its energy resources. But, if in the final analysis, Europe's dependence on the Middle East provides the central problem of energy over the coming decades, there seems little reason for optimism at present that it is a problem which is going to be easily solved.

EUROPEAN ENERGY POLICIES

Commission officials, and some commentators, have greeted the dawn of a new era of co-ordinated European policy towards oil, with European Government pressing in to take over where the declining oil companies will leave off. And the view is not altogether unfounded. The 'energy crisis' has put new confidence into the Commission, as industry plans and consultative documents are taken down from the top shelves and the member states instead of ignoring them actually encourage their formulation and implementation.

On the question of storage the will is undoubtedly there. Europe as a whole will almost certainly follow up the idea of offering the Middle Eastern producers favourable trade deals with credit backing. The urge to see greater co-ordination of market investment will be strengthened. But the basic problem of developing a positive European policy towards relations with the oil producers remains that of defining the best instrument to carry it out. It was on this question, and the definition of a community oil company, that successive attempts by France to galvanise the EEC into action met with equally successive objections by Holland, with its more internationally orientated view of the oil trade. And this stumbling block remains as strong as ever. The entry of Britain has added new strength to the Dutch cause and has created an even more even balance between the host countries of major oil companies and those, like Italy and France, without.

A number of recent statements by both Community officials and national oil companies have made it clear that Europeans are now increasingly distrustful of the US and US oil companies in the present energy situation and no longer feel that their best interests are necessarily protected by the international oil companies. This even applies to some extent within the UK. But, in looking for alternatives, the answers become less clear cut. A direct relationship between the producing and consuming countries would only work effectively if the consumer gave a guaranteed market to the producer and the producer gave guaranteed supplies to the consumer. Italy, France and Germany have gone some way towards assuring at least a portion of their markets are in the hands of national oil companies and one would expect to see those companies substantially increasing their crude oil sources in line with their markets. But this move will probably be limited.

The Franco-Algerian experience has shown the dangers of any country becoming too dependent on a limited source of oil, and this type of bilateral relationship tends to increase the vulnerability of oil supplies. At the same time, a dirigiste policy towards the market runs counter to the Community's declared aims and could involve endless problems of retaliation against, for example, French companies in the UK or Germany. Nor is it by any means clear that this is what the producers really want. As long as they can pick and choose, the US and Japan would seem more attractive markets for them both in terms of downstream investment and crude oil sales.

The European Commission itself would like to go further along this course for the area as a whole. But the UK in particular is likely to resist it. BP and Shell now have a very considerable stake in the US, as do other British companies, and neither the UK nor Holland could afford to go too far along a route which would be bound to become increasingly anti-American, while the UK is in any case determined to avoid ideas of rights of European companies beginning to nibble at its own North Sea assets. On the oil side, at least, Europe has little to offer the UK, rather the reverse and the UK would seem bound to use its cards to protect its own international interests.

This is not to say that Europe will do nothing to meet the problems posed by oil security. But it does seem more likely that its moves in the field of producer relationships will be carried out on an individual country level with co-ordination proceeding on a bilateral rather than a federal basis. France and the UK, with Germany kept well informed, are already moving towards a common Middle East foreign policy on such issues as Israel and one would expect to see this continuing. On more detailed questions, the general scenario would seem to be agreement not to tread on each others' toes. The UK has very considerable influence in the Gulf. France has created strong ties with Iraq of late. Each will continue along these lines, involving trade more and more with oil, but keeping it within a national rather than community concept.

Such a development implies gradual rather than dramatic changes in oil relationships. But then, at the end of the day, this may well be as much as the European countries can hope to achieve. There can be no final solution to the problem of security of oil supplies outside of relieving Europe of its dependence on them. Until this is achieved, Europe will have to live under the shadow of growing US oil imports and growing producer power, dealing with it as best it can.

Discussion

Mr C. L. Goodacre (Consultant):

1. Let us face it, we are in a big mess from what we have been told in the last two days. This seems to indicate the world's oil refinery industry is, by force of circumstances, generated in part by US environmentalist pursuers, now at the mercy of the OPEC organisation!

2. What we have heard about energy futures for the major industrial countries is disquieting to say the least, on future crude oil supplies to the refineries of these countries who temporarily seem to have 'out run the constable', in that they have not got the crude oil and it seems doubtful if they can generate acceptable money to pay for what they need from the producers, without serving an arms race in OPEC. The table is running against them in a sellers' market.

3. It seems an 'in house' solution must be found, *i.e.* a full range distillates refinery that does not need crude oil. *Where there is a will there is a way!*

4. Can the world's oil refining industry swallow its pride and turn to the coal industry for the solution with that industry's almost limitless resources of energy; for example a rapid re-appraisal of such processes as the Fischer–Tropsch process, using trick modern technology *i.e.* catalysts, etc.?

5. This FT process, according to Weil and Lane, Keith *et al.*, from US coal reserves alone can provide 1000 billion tons of synthetic oil from which any distillate product can be made; this means 200 years supply at 1980 rates.

6. For example 1 ton of bituminous coal will produce 2·5 brls of 85 mm 92 RM motor gasoline and other products, or 50 000 tons of coal will produce 100 000 brls/day gasoline, with an 8000-man task force, which is not much different from petroleum production methods (1950 figures).

7. This gasoline at 1950 prices cost 8 US cents/USG, now with 23 years of technology behind us, can such figures be improved upon?

8. The FT process 30 years ago, as developed by our opponents, was considered such a strategic menace that we had to resort to violence to destroy such sources of production, otherwise we might have lost out? To do this we had to use 2000 bombers, at an astronomical cost, probably $4 billion, with the sacrifice of 5000 lives. So can this formidable opponent of crude oil now be our salvation?

9. It is going to cost a lot of steel and money, but it amounts to taking in our washing, *i.e.* doing the job at home!

10. We can thus show our friends, who are sitting on most of the crude oil we need, that we can do without them in part, if they make matters too difficult for us.

213

We can build political refineries such as FT, or other synthetic plants, to balance our energy books and maintain the world's monetary system in balance.

Perhaps, therefore, we should think before branching into atomic power.

Mr G. Chandler (President, Institute of Petroleum): Could I, while our speaker is thinking, make a comment. I imagine that if Mr Goodacre's policy was implemented, every country in industrial competition would have to follow it, otherwise the loner could, when others have cheaper sources of energy available, become highly uncompetitive. It is either all doing it or doing at one's peril as an individual nation.

There is one other point I'd like to make: Mr A. Hamilton did say that little work had been done on the percentage of GNP that energy takes up. France is probably the only country, because of its historical statistics, in which you can really see this. And in France energy as a percentage of gross national product fell from, say 1945 to the present day, by 10% to about 7% because of the substitution of coal by oil and so on. Making estimates, even taking very high price rises for energy, only brings back the percentage of GNP to what it was in the post-war period. I think a very great deal more research is needed on this sort of thing as, even taking a very pessimistic view of a very high tax take, the high cost of energy does not seem to make it intolerable in GNP terms, though, of course, it does pose balance of payments problems so far as it is imported energy.

Mr A. Hamilton: Well, I can't say anything on the technical matters but my main remarks concerned consumer governments' thinking towards the producers. Obviously the development of alternative sources is going to be something that the consumer can do and he's going to look very closely at. The only remark I wanted to make is, again, I think it's one of the distressing facts of Europe that it seems to have found difficulties in getting together on this sort of thing. If you take nuclear power, you get into the situation of very considerable argument between Germany, Britain and France over such matters because we have all got a fair amount of money invested in one form or another. One problem is going to be that investment in individual countries, both state and private, in various alternative forms of energy, is already such that the consumer governments will squabble among themselves in Europe as to what is the right course to be taken. Because of this conflict, I think it will be some years on before the EEC commission takes over the initiative.

Mr J. M. C. Bishop (Phillips Petroleum Co. Ltd): Mr Hamilton foresees European governments carving up between them the job of negotiating with producing country governments. As Professor Edith Penrose stressed, the people with the knowledge of the industry are in the companies. What role therefore does Mr Hamilton see for the oil companies in his intergovernmental negotiation era?

Mr A. Hamilton: I didn't suggest that we should try to carve it up, because we don't have a cake to carve up in the first place. But I think one thing I didn't bring up strongly enough is that the consumer governments in Europe are veering away from the old feeling (in Britain and other countries) of regarding the interests of all oil companies as a pretty good safeguard for their own interests. I think we saw this coming out very clearly in the Iraq nationalisation crisis.

I think most consumer governments now, including slowly but surely the British government, are beginning to feel that the producing companies are becoming merely the junior partners of the producing countries. The companies just don't have the ability to fight the producers any more. The problem is that the consumer governments have nothing to replace the companies with, so how this is going to turn out will depend from country to country. But one of the direct actions that will develop from this is that the consumer government will attempt much more strongly to control the way investment is handled in Europe. However, because of the conflict between countries who are hosts to the international companies, like Britain and France, which we saw in this recent meeting, I think that it's not going to be on a totally European scale, I think that it is going to be on an individual scale.

I think a number of continental countries are also very worried about the fact that the American crisis is for the first time bringing the possibility that an American company operating in Europe could find itself with a divided interest of where to put its supplies, and they're not at all sure that these companies will in fact push them into Europe. In other words they may well push them into America for higher profits—it is their home country after all. Whether these feelings are fair or not, they are the present feelings. But if you assume, as I assume, that what will really happen in Europe is a state of inaction, I think you will get things coming along very much as they are.

In other words, if you got the Libyans nationalising tomorrow, the French and Italians would be quite happy to step in. The British would make a lot of fuss, and you'd get what happened in Iran. On the other hand, I don't see the British going in for intergovernmental relations. What the governments are thinking of is not direct state-to-state deals on oil as such, but an attempt to gain influence in a producing country and use such influence as they have to ensure that the oil comes through.

Mr G. Chandler: You mentioned the fear of companies diverting oil from their traditional outlets because of their ultimate national affiliation. I think there is a very strong incentive for companies with investments in their traditional outlets to go on feeding those investments because of the fear of what might happen if they did not. I believe there is also a fear, and this particularly among Japanese whose industrial and social ethos is a very different one from that of the United States and Europe, that the host-governments—that is the American government, the British government, the French government and the Dutch government—might try and impose pressures on companies of those nationalities to divert supplies.

The question I'd like to ask is, assuming you can get governmental co-operation, would a self-denying ordinance by these governments that they will not put pressure on companies of their national identity to divert supplies help the situation? Particularly in relation to Japan, because the Japanese working in a Japanese company outside Japan feels he owes his first affiliation to his home country, this might not be so marked with a national in an American, British, French or Dutch company.

Mr A. Hamilton: Well, it would happen, and the day I look forward to most in this issue is when the oil companies assume a pure offtake role, and that is what I would foresee. In this case, I think the oil companies would end up better than anyone else, because they have the expertise, the management, as well as the existing investment to manage a pure trading situation. I think the great problem for the oil industry is that it's in production as well. Once you get the situation of being offtakers, you get a fair trading situation in which, in a situation where supplies might be tight, the oil companies will manage very well. What we're really talking about is something much wider—is the role of the multi-national companies and whether they can continue to be multi-national or whether they'll become increasingly national. I don't think anyone has the answer to this yet. Oil is the one area that may be the first to crumble amongst the multi-nationals, or it may be the one area where people don't allow things to happen because the resources are too important to countries to have a breakdown of supplies.

The self-relying ordinance is what the British government is pushing very strongly at present and it obviously would do a great deal, but if you got into this situation, I don't see how you could avoid facing up to the fact that the Italians and the French would not be unhappy to step in. Where this might be effective is in pure bilateral negotiation or conversation between the French and British. That would include the whole range of issues outside energy, if the British say to the French very strongly over Libya for example that they are not to go in there and mess it up; then success depends on what counter offer is made on the North Sea in regard to CFP.

I think the great danger of the Common Market is that its history so far has been a continued trade-off between various factions. Thus you get agricultural against industrial policy and this is why it makes it very difficult to calculate what an individual country is going to do. You get the DTI saying it will defend North Sea oil to the last drop. When it comes to the crunch it's the Prime Minister who is worried about the next election. If the French come along to the Prime Minister and say we can offer you a degree of flexibility on agricultural policy but in return we will require some give on your part in the North Sea, is he going to refuse? Whichever Prime Minister it is, is he going to say, no the North Sea is outside this, or is he going to say, well look at the way beef prices have been going, we will have to do something about this? I think these kind of factors are often forgotten.

Mr C. M. Dalley (Iraq Petroleum Co. Ltd): Aren't we confusing two things, one is the so-called ownership of concessions which is a thing of the past virtually, and the other is the distribution of the available oil throughout Europe; I believe myself that we should no longer worry about the ownership of concessions because the way in which the whole movement is going will mean that all companies will be virtually in a position of offtakers at the jetty, under different systems of contract.

So what we are now faced with is how to distribute the oil satisfactorily throughout Europe, and this can only be done by consumer governments. In my view this is absolutely outside the scope of the oil industry. I believe the countries, including Britain and Holland, particularly concerned with the international oil companies would welcome this as much, if not more than the net consumers such as Germany. Do you agree?

Mr A. Hamilton: Well, I think not. One of the most fascinating speeches recently was the chairman of BP's statement in the annual report, where almost for the first time a chairman of a major oil company virtually pleaded for government intervention. The question is, how are we going to do this. Is it going to be through governmental control of international oil companies or is it going to be by direct governmental control of the market through state oil companies.

The danger of this is that if you say governmental control of the oil companies, unless there is some agreement between the major oil consuming areas you are going to get the problem of whether a multi-national company is responsible to all its customers or just to its host government. I am not nearly as sanguine as some people seem to be about the prospects of governments intervening to both control investment and also the way supplies are going, through pressure on the oil companies, because then I think you are going to get into a terrible muddle.

Mr G. Chandler: Could I ask Professor Penrose if she would like to add anything to this. I find myself in very great agreement with what Mr Hamilton has said and I think he is right in raising this question of the role of the multi-national companies themselves with their loyalties and the way they operate. I don't really agree with the statement that he made earlier that the Japanese companies considered the host country's interests but not the American or British companies. That is their primary responsibility. It seems to me that now, particularly in Europe, there are so many trade-offs involved that the companies will do the operating job but the governments will make the policy and the policy will affect prices, investment and everything else, but it will not yet be on a European basis. It seems to me to be a very realistic approach all through, and I have the feeling that pressure of events may push them a little bit more rapidly than Mr Hamilton is inclined to allow from the point of view of how quickly Europe can get together on this matter. I find that in retrospect one often finds, when the heat is on, that things work out much more quickly than it looks as if they possibly could in prospect.

Mr N. White (Hambros Bank): Mr Hamilton made two or three comments relating to government direction of investment and I also note that Professor Penrose again referred to this in her contribution. I wonder whether they could tell us what they envisage might happen.

Mr A. Hamilton: I think there will be control, not only where, but how many refineries are built. This is one of the strongest suggestions of the EEC Commission, but it has got into a lot of difficulties about definitions. The proposal that all companies would have to give it information about their future investment and various incentivies, etc. might be offered.

It got into a terrible debacle because of the difficulties of defining what was a European company so that I don't know that the EEC Commission will be taking very strong steps, but I do see control of where refineries are put and how much is developed.

What I also see is that governments will demand that the companies keep them much more fully informed about the flow of oil and that they will then intervene to say where they want it to go. Now the British have changed their attitudes upon the North Sea. The British did not produce legislation to control where the North Sea oil flowed. I sense very strongly now that they regret they did not. This would of course bring complications about whether it would conflict with EEC rules or not. But I think on the North Sea, for instance, the British will start to control, both under pressure from the other EEC countries and for their own sake, because they will also have to answer to the public if a large volume of North Sea oil disappears over the horizon of the Atlantic. With that kind of situation the government takes a much more direct interest in companies like BP, and where British oil flows.

CHAPTER 15

Planning for the Future

D. C. ION

formerly British Petroleum Co. Ltd, London, UK

INTRODUCTION

This paper is concerned with planning for the future in the light of the available preprints of the papers for this meeting and, to some degree, on the discussions we have had.

I will consider the subject in the four main areas of supply, transportation, conversion and utilisation because, whilst the meeting's programme nominally moved from shorter to longer term factors, these factors are interdependent, and there has not been any such clear demarcation in either the papers or the discussions. The presentations and discussions have brough out new ideas and facts but there has not been time to absorb all their implications, and I cannot therefore attempt to summarise the whole meeting.

Affecting all four areas of the industry there are, of course, at the moment, two factors, concern for the environment and the change from apparent over-supply to apparent under-supply. These two factors spawn two other factors, firstly increased concern for resource conservation, which will lead to emphasis on greater efficiency in recovery, conversion and use, greater selectivity in end-use and higher energy costs, with the consumer having eventually to pay for his choice of environmental quality, and, secondly the increasing interdependence of the energy industries which will become more real as well as apparent.

As one considers the four main areas of the energy field it will become plain that, although technically there is still much to be done—in some fields a great deal to be done—it is the politico-economic factors which will be more significant in the next decade or so, for conventional, non-conventional and alternative energy sources.

SUPPLY

The resource base
We can be, and have been in the past two days assured that, world-wide, there is an abundance of the primary energy sources.

Very large deposits of coal are known and can be extracted in solid form or, in certain circumstances, energy can be extracted in liquid or gaseous form. The inhibitors are, in some areas, restraints imposed by concern for damage to the environment and, elsewhere, economics.

Known petroleum reserves can be extracted but need to be replenished by new discoveries. The need for such is more obvious than for coal, partly because of the difference of materials, coal being static and oil and gas dynamic, but also because of the differences in the reserve concepts.[1]

Crude oil and natural gas have both technical and environmental problems as exploration moves into more hostile areas, particularly deep offshore, but these are technically solvable. In addition to the conventional petroleum resources there are the very large back-up supplies available from coal, tar sands, oil shales and very heavy oil deposits. For these sources there are no problems in discovery and no major technical or environmental problems in most aspects. There are, however, economic problems, on conventional accounting and some projects may require government or multi-government funding.

Nuclear energy sources are widespread and abundant and though exploration for new reserves should continue, there are few technical problems in exploration or production.

There is no lack of supply of other primary energy forms, like solar energy, but there are major technical difficulties in harnessing and problems of location.

Production

The current concern about the supply of energy has developed in the USA and the communications media have emphasised that concern. As recently as June, 1972, the National Petroleum Council said '. . . the subject of energy supply is treated with complacency. Most customers take for granted the continued availability of all they require'. Hence the media have probably performed a worthwhile job in focussing attention on the problem but the pendulum must not be allowed to swing to the extreme of hysteria.

There is not yet a world energy shortage; not even a petroleum shortage. However, there might be if, for political reasons, one or more of the major producers stopped producing. The shut-in reserves of the USA, which twice forestalled a shortage, no longer exist and volumes are now too great for rapid substitutes to be provided. It is the large volumes and the exponential extrapolations of demand by some writers which cause concern in the absence of categorical reassurances of new discoveries, which cannot be given.

In the USA the ratio of published proved oil reserves to production[3] fell from 1900 to 1925 from over 40 to about 11 but since then has continued in a band between 12 and 15 with the 1972 figure still being almost 12. However, USA production of crude oil and natural gas liquids is now only 68·5% of the domestic demand and the shortfall has to be met by net imports. USA production has fallen from 61% of the world total in 1938 to 20% in 1972 but, even more significantly, the USA has now only 6·2% of the world's published proved reserves but 30% of its consumption.[4] Only recently have people in the USA become aware of these figures although the trends have been recognised by the oil industry world-wide.

In 1949 Dr King Hubbert illustrated to a United Nations Conference on Energy Resources that fossil fuels were of finite size and exhaustible. Although one objected, then and since, to his conservatism and to his apparent obsession with the logistic curve, without due regard for human ingenuity, he, and many others since then, including myself, have stressed that American domestic production must peak, plateau and then decline. These warnings went unheeded; this is a failure to convince, not a victory for those who said so. The point has now been taken and effort is now required to ensure that the USA does not act in some irrational manner to right the situation as they now, suddenly, see it. President Nixon's message of 18 April, 1973, gives hope that this will not happen.

However, it has been said that a Presidential crisis in the USA is a peculiar phenomenon in that its declaration makes its existence and its solution inevitable. The President can then deploy the full might of the nation, as in war. For instance, a similar effort applied to oil shales as to the building of T2 tankers in the Second World War could produce a significant amount of oil in three years; similarly, under such rules, coal production could move from 600 to 1700 million tons in three years. Is President Nixon moving towards a 'Presidential crisis'? Might one feature be to encourage Europe and Japan to adopt crisis attitudes and invest $10 thousand million in Canadian tar sands and the USA reciprocate with a similar sum in US oil shales?

There may, however, be a more immediate and practical danger in the apparent assumption in President Nixon's message that an increase in financial incentives will, automatically and immediately, bring forth new domestic petroleum discoveries. Explorers find oil, not accountants. The explorers in the US domestic industry have been inhibited from taking big risks for almost twenty years. I suggest that to change 'tame tigers' into 'wildcats' cannot be done overnight and that disappointment after over-optimistic expectations might result in ill-judged over-reaction.

The world situation outside the USA does not seem to be so serious as to warrant any 'crash programme'. The world ratio of published proved reserves to production also fell from about 33 in 1900 to 15 in 1925 but rose to about 37 from 1935 to 1955 and was 34·4 in 1972.[4] World production has risen from 1654 million barrels in 1935 to over 18 000 million barrels in 1972. However, looking ahead, there is no doubt that there will need to be tremendous effort to maintain a reasonable reserves/production ratio.

Professor Penrose has discussed the factors which may affect the supply from the Middle East, where the problem for the producers is not yet one of scarcity but rather the optimum use of their abundance. At the other end of the scale, Japan is almost entirely dependent for its energy on imported petroleum from the Middle East. Japan is not embroiled in current Middle East political problems and feels that it has a special position. The Minister for International Trade and Industry, Yasuhiro Nakasone, on 10 May, 1973, again stressed that Japan would not participate in any consortium of consuming countries; he wants co-operation, not confrontation. Only in the last few years has Europe seen a hope of indigenous oil supplies of significance, though even the optimists at the moment forecast a 1980 production of about a fifth of Europe's demand in 1980, being 4–5 mbd production for 10–12 thousand million barrels of proved reserves to a consumption of about 23 mbd.

The USSR has doubled its production of crude oil over the past ten years to more than 7 mbd. Now they are seeking outside technical knowledge and even funds to increase production. Despite the great theoretical potential of the USSR it would not seem probable for them to develop a surplus which would significantly affect the world position. Indeed one recent estimate[6] was for a deficit of 100 million tons of crude by 1980 in USSR and Eastern Europe.

There is no doubt that other areas, as Dr Gaskell said, including the Arctic area, Indonesia and offshore Pacific Asia, will be explored and that oil will be found, but no one can say how much.

History tells us that we move forward in supply in sudden steps.[7] To attain the next leap forward the only preparation on the supply side is to explore more vigorously and produce more efficiently more of the oil-in-place from conventional sources whilst gaining practical experience in extraction from non-conventional sources. Few doubt that costs will rise and therefore prices. Will $6 per barrel of crude and 75c per cu ft of gas be the standard prices in the USA in 1985? How much non-conventional oil then becomes economically viable?

I have not discussed the magnitude of reserves but I would like to comment that, despite the great difficulty, there must soon be a far greater attempt than in the past to quantify known reserves and attempt to estimate the amount of oil recoverable at increasing price levels, in the same way that OECD have attempted for uranium[8] and the National Petroleum Council for US oil and gas supplies.[9] Indeed Rothkopf and de Vries were moving towards this in their paper to the meeting.

TRANSPORTATION

Petroleum is dominant in inter-regional energy flows. From 1929 to 1965 the share of liquid fuels has increased from 59 to 93% of the total inter-regional energy flows and has increased absolutely by over 17 times. The world's oil tanker fleet has grown from less than 10 million dwt in 1950 to over 200 million dwt in 1973 with more than a quarter consisting of VLCCs of over 175 000 dwt.

The long distance transportation of petroleum, as liquid or gas, by pipeline or tanker, presents no technical problems except in certain specialised circumstances of sensitive environments. Between 1940 and 1970 the maximum diameter of petroleum pipelines increased from 75 to 120 cm, the maximum length from 700 to 2700 km. Some 15 years ago I remember Lord Strathalmond expressing surprise to Steve Bechtel Sr. that he was still measuring pipe diameters in inches and not yards. Problems still arise but there is no reason to doubt solutions will be found.

The current example of a sensitive environment is, of course, the delay by at least three years of construction of the Trans-Alaska pipeline. That delay is not all loss, because the research effort required to answer the objections of the environmentalists has undoubtedly ensured that the line, when built, will be nearer to the oilman's self-interested ideal of never seeing more oil than is necessary to test its chemical and physical properties. The knowledge and experience from this line will mean a big step forward in conquering the Arctic, where some in the USSR consider lies half the world's remaining undiscovered reserves. Problems of laying submarine pipelines are also being beaten.

The ability to handle and build oil tankers up to 1 million dwt is to hand. Restrictions on loading and unloading tankers to ensure maximum gain from economy of scale exist but can be overcome in a sufficient number of places to create no major problems. Problems of safety at sea, avoidance of collision accidents and remedial action after oil spills have been the subject of so much effort by the oil industry, the Inter-governmental Maritime Consultative Organisation, tanker owners, governments and harbour and coastal authorities that again, as with pipelines, only in areas of high environmental sensitivity, as the Straits of Juan de Fuca, British Columbia, are there likely to be external restrictions on planning. However, both pipelines and major tanker terminals are fixed points which can crystallise the pattern of both input and output, reduce flexibility and act as a planning parameter to new energy systems networks.

Developments have been rapid in the last ten years in Europe and the UK of VLCC terminals, pipeline networks (crude, products and gas) and refining and distribution centres. Oil and gas lines from the North Sea are changing the pattern. In the USA and Canada they have had for some years a complex pattern of oil and gas lines; amendments with lines from the Arctic, the Athabasca Tar Sands and the Green River Shales of Colorado may become significant, but even the proposed development of deep water oil ports will not really affect the petroleum transportation network. Similarly, the import of LNG by sea to these networks is not going to affect them much even though by 1980 there may be 100 ocean-going ships with sizes ranging up to 200 000 cubic metres capacity or more, carrying exports from the USSR and Africa.

Whilst the general network patterns may be set, there may be shifts in ownership. Shipping companies currently own 65% of crude oil tankers and oil companies 35%. As producing countries increase their participation downstream, they may well increase their ownership and so economic leverage to a significant extent. The cost and the alignment of new major pipelines may involve multi-national financing and ownership.

The movement of petroleum is a movement of energy competitive with other energy forms. As a liquid or gas, petroleum has the advantage over solid coal, and even in the USA coal-slurry lines have not yet beaten bulk unit trains. Its bulk puts petroleum at a disadvantage with uranium. Relative transportation costs and, more recently, environmental restraints have shifted the optimum location patterns of electricity generating stations, and in some local circumstances there may be a conflict between the siting of refineries and that of power stations. Similarly future petroleum networks may be affected, but probably for some time more locally than strategically, by the development of long distance DC transmissions which, ideally, would form trans-continental grids of superconducting lines with massive power-flows using to advantage the diversity factors of distant networks.[10]

There seems every chance that for the next twenty years or more the general pattern of petroleum transportation will be the most important in the energy scene. After that there may be a declining increase in share as the main uses of petroleum move from the primary energy field.

CONVERSION

The pressures for the utilisation of coal in the next fifteen years are going to be strong, as Mr Hamilton mentions for Europe. As an accessible fuel indigenous to and the historic mainspring of the advanced industrial countries of the USA and Europe, coal has obvious advantages, but also problems both in deep mining and in environmental objections to strip-mining and the emission of sulphur compounds. However, in the UK, Mr Derek Ezra is reported as saying that there is 'high probability that coal will be cheaper than oil for steam-raising by 1980'.[11]

Mr Broadbent dealt with what have become almost the main themes of the meeting, namely that:

i. Present trends cannot continue or an energy gap will be created,
ii. We need all energy resources, coal, gas, oil, nuclear and others,
iii. We should take an integrated view of energy, using each source in its rightful place and, where possible, integrate research and development.

Professor Leslie has dealt at this meeting in depth with the conversion problems in the nuclear energy field and in summary considers that 'if oil prices increase in the way most people expect, nuclear power will be clearly cheaper by 1985 . . . the present-day cost difference between the two methods of electrical generation is small'.

On the petroleum side there would seem to be no technical problems in refining to provide main products, except for those problems involved in removing or dissipating noxious or polluting gases and particulates, without noise and in plants which do not offend the public eye. The techniques are available but the cost must be more closely gauged to the social price the consumer will pay and, as yet, there is no real estimate of that price. Effort will, however, be increasingly necessary to shape products to demands for higher efficiency in use. There will also, undoubtedly, with time, be an evolution into other products with changing refinery patterns and plant.

UTILISATION

Demand

Simple extrapolations of past population growth and energy use lead to the 'doomwatchers' or 'Neo-Malthusian' forecasts of rapid exhaustion of the world's energy resources. This meeting illustrates a more reasonable attitude to the problem. Forecasts by 'mental models' are being increasingly augmented by 'mathematical models', but, as Rothkopf and de Vries so well illustrate in their paper, much research is required before technological advances and behavioural patterns can be incorporated with sufficient precision for reliability. Greater precision is needed to be able to benefit from such models when attempting to look into the future and balance growth and conservation. The point must be stressed that absolute precision is impossible when dealing with independent factors altered by the summation of individual decisions. Mathematical models have one great advantage over mental models in that the whole programme can be on record and a new operator can see exactly how results were reached. Mental models are unique and not transferable—hence there is appalling waste of knowledge/experience/intuition/expertise when mental model operators move on to other tasks.

Research is very necessary, in order to gain greater precision in estimating energy demand, population growth (including the relationship between growth of income per capita and fertility rate), growth of income and energy demand, the effect on energy consumption of the price of energy relative to the price of other resources, the impact of urbanisation, the quantification of the social costs of different types of pollution and the responsiveness of producers and consumers to price changes.[12] There is an impressive list of areas of insufficient knowledge in the basic assumptions on which demand forecasts can be made. This should be both a spur to increased research effort and also a warning against any but the most cautious use of present day rough models.

A minor point may be relevant here and applicable possibly more to mental models; there is still a regrettable lack of standardisation of unit nomenclature. Even in the papers for this meeting there is a lack of uniformity which hinders understanding and communication. Finally on this subject I would stress again that all forecasts, particularly about petroleum, must be on a continuing basis because of the dynamism of the industry.

Increased efficiency
One of the undoubted aspects of the immediate future is the call for greater efficiency in use, which has been discussed here in the Alkema and Newland paper; and I do not agree with any profligate waste policy.

It is understood that in Switzerland there is a regulation in draft form empowering inspection of all energy appliances and the imposition of fines for waste. President Nixon on his message of 18 April, 1973, notes that he is establishing an Office of Energy Conservation and directing the Department of Commerce to develop a voluntary system of energy efficiency labels for major home appliances.

However, it is only by a major change in public attitude that conservation can be really effective. My personal experience of energy shortages during the Second World War makes me instinctively turn off the light when I leave an empty room. The next generation have no such reaction. Two weeks ago at a formal dinner in Japan, making conversation with the wife of my Japanese host, through an interpreter, I remarked that my wife always felt that bright lights were a strain on the ladies. The reply was that in the olden days candles were Japan's only form of illumination and now with modern industrialisation the brightness of the lights was a status symbol. My further remark, that the need for conservation of energy might soon lead to a more modern concept of values, evoked the immediate reply that the power companies would not like that. A reversal of materialistic, energy-wasteful status goals in Japan, where there is now, within 20 years, as much waste as in the USA, is obviously a formidable task, but one which obviously is necessary and, one suggests, should be started as fast as possible. This is a world-wide problem and one where governments will have to mount educational programmes as well as regulations.

Increased selectivity in end-use

The threat of energy shortage, the increasing cost of the raw material and the substitution of other energy sources for primary needs will lead to increased selectivity in the end-use of petroleum.

The main effort in research and development will be towards the greater utilisation of the chemical characteristics of petroleum for secondary industries. Proteins from oil may have been a spectacular but not necessarily the last of such developments. The petrochemical field offers very great scope. Alkema and Newland note the low energy cost of plastics and obviously the development of biodegradable plastics for temporary containers would remove the objectionable pollution disadvantages.

Such changes will have an effect on the number of barrels of oil required or, put another way, on the effective size of the barrel. 'To meet the changing pattern of market demand the skill of the refiner/research chemist expands the barrel but not all barrels equally. The statistical device of converting barrels into thermal units underestimates both the achievement and the potential of petroleum and its reserves. Seventy years ago kerosine was the only marketable product' and the size of the barrel was therefore the size of the kerosine content—contrast that with the present number of petroleum products from the barrel—'Hence one might say that the barrel in 1900 was not the same size as the barrel of 1967 and that of the 2000 AD barrel will again be different.'[1]

The subject of increased selectivity of end-use is a matter of interest to the other energy industries and we have the benefit of Mr Brookes's paper, 'Towards the All-Electric Economy', which illustrates the interdependence of the energy industries, and we have had the thought-provoking paper by Professor Ubbelohde.

INTERDEPENDENCE OF ENERGY RESOURCES AND INDUSTRIES

For the past hundred years there has been great, sometimes bitter rivalry between the industries based on different energy resources. This has been healthy. Competition has spurred on research and development into technological innovations. However, there were disadvantages. The British coal industry, when it felt that it was fighting for survival ten years ago, antagonised the oil industry by the exaggerated attacks on the size of petroleum reserves without appreciating their character. The nuclear energy industry in its infancy made some very sweeping claims and accusations. Now the British coal industry knows that 200 million tons annual production is not the floor of viability. The nuclear energy industry did not take that sudden expected leap forward and now has a much more sober attitude. The British Gas Corporation now knows something of the petroleum industry for it is wedded to natural gas. The oil industry planners, if not the salesmen, have been saying for twenty years that there is room for all in the satisfying of the increasing demand for energy.

I hope, with Mr Broadbent, that the next decade will see closer collaboration, a lessening of petulant outbursts of jealousy between the energy industries. Forty years ago geologists and geophysicists were at daggers drawn in the oil game but, in some companies faster than in others, they began to realise that their skills were complementary and interdependent.[13] Let us hope that the energy industries will realise this rapidly.

There may be a field here in which the Institute of Petroleum might play as successful a part as it has in the environmental field in encouraging co-operation between different interests, the oil and water industries, local and central government agencies, and research establishments, and in the international field in encouraging co-operation between the different petroleum associations in Europe. In the USA the American Association of Petroleum Geologists, particularly at an Annual Meeting some four years ago, stressed the need for petroleum geologists to think of themselves as energy geologists. Some oil companies in the USA have diversified into coal and/or uranium interests. Yet I suggest that the general attitude of mind in Britain, with its appreciation of consents procedures, may give greater opportunity for faster practical collaboration than elsewhere. One example may illustrate one of many areas of mutual interest. I have mentioned the need for research into the different forms of pollution. All energy industries are involved. The CEGB has no monopoly of interest or experience with tall stacks or with thermal pollution of water or with landscaping, yet I attended a meeting the other day at which it appeared that they considered this was so. Such attitudes must be changed if we are to make the best of our natural energy resources.

In this general area I agree with Lord Zuckerman, as reported from his Stockton Lecture to the London Business School, 23 March, 1973,[14] 'Only better technology can eliminate the undesired after-effects of bad technology and it can only do so when the necessary resources become available. . . . Today the exhaustion of resources, pollution and the environment, and population growth seem to have taken the place of the hydrogen bomb as the prevailing social fear. But we dare not despair. We will deal with these problems—because we have to'.

I suggest that the necessary resources can best be made available by closer collaboration amongst the energy industries, though there still remain many technical problems for the petroleum industry to tackle itself, many of which have been indicated in the past few days.

CONCLUSION

In conclusion, I revert to my earlier premise that it is the politico-economic factors rather than technical factors which will have more significance over the next ten or so years.

In general it would seem that, in planning for the future, mental models, which in fact we have all been building up in the past few days, are still more important than mathematical models, for which more research is necessary to obtain more precise numbers. In considering potential politico-economic factors we are in the least precise and quantifiable area of all.

There appears to be a growing feeling that the deployment of effort to discover and utilise in the optimum manner the world's energy resources is now beyond the capabilities of individuals, companies, single industries or even single nations. The first problem would therefore seem to be how and where to start useful co-operation.

Before putting forward suggestions for discussion, I must declare some underlying prejudices, namely,

(i) I prefer to tackle international politico-economic problems initially through technical co-operation and not in the reverse order,

(ii) I prefer to start collaboration informally, prove a need, show progress and then use existing organisations if possible, rather than set up a new organisation and then wonder what it should do,

(iii) I have not from this meeting gained any impression that,

(a) the existing industries, complex and varied though their structures may now be, are not capable of constantly adapting to the changes we are now experiencing or can foresee, nor that

(b) any world organisation would be capable of handling world energy policy during the remainder of this century.

I would now like to make the following points:

1. On the supply side there appears at the moment to be sufficient opposition to the polarisation of producing and consuming or democratic and controlled economy countries for there to be better chances of bilateral or multinational co-operation than of bloc confrontation.

There is, of course, the outstanding problem of the current lack of definition of jurisdiction of the exploitation of the seabed beyond the edge of the continental shelf, but maybe the long discussions in the UN will be sufficiently mutually educative for a mutually satisfactory solution.

No single country at the moment appears to be in a sufficiently strong position to act unilaterally without doing more harm to itself than to others.

The chances seem best therefore for gradual evolution of existing trends, rather than dramatic revolution, even though there are dangers which one hopes are obvious to all. Dangers are from uncertain factors such as changes in the supply mechanism as host countries assume a controlling role in their oil production; from the possibility of the USA, with its growing domestic energy deficit, outmanoevring others for supplies from the Eastern hemisphere; from the increasing competition for oil supplies world-wide causing friction, first among the consuming countries—the buyers—and then among the producing countries—the sellers; and even from the conservation policies which certain oil producing countries may decide to follow as their surplus funds from their oil revenues build up.

2. On the transportation side there is increasing co-operation on safety and environmental aspects and this may be expected to continue without any new initiatives, even though ownership shifts may take place.

3. In the broad field of conversion there would seem to be immediate possibilities for active co-operation. President Nixon's message of 18 April contains references to some such co-operation. Whilst one might not expect

investment in oil shale research and development to be an obvious first choice for surplus Arab oil money, yet Arab countries have considerable heavy oil deposits which technical advances would enable them to exploit to better advantage. The USSR also, of course, has large oil-shale deposits in its energy-poor western side which technical breakthroughs should enable them to exploit. On the conventional refining side the producers should be as eager to ensure optimum conversion of petroleum to meet consumer needs as the consuming countries or their companies and so be willing to invest in research and development.

4. It is, however, in the field of increased efficiency in the utilisation of energy and the elimination of waste that there is, in my view, the greatest possibility for co-operation. In every developed industrial country there would seem to be possible practical and immediate co-operation in education, research and development between the energy industries and between those industries and the government. By using existing organisations this effort could widen rapidly to broader areas or regions and, through organisations such as the Economic Council of the United Nations Organisation, could achieve direct and full collaboration with the governments of developing countries, which lack energy reserves. This would result in a better appreciation and therefore a wiser deployment of the world's energy resources for all mankind.

REFERENCES

1. D. C. Ion (1967). 'The significance of World petroleum reserves', in *Proceedings of the 7th World Petroleum Congress, Mexico*, Review Paper 2, Applied Science, London.
2. 'Outlook for energy in the USA to 1980', Nat. Petrol. Council, Washington, p. 37, 1972.
3. D. C. Ion (1956). 'Ore resources in the next half century', IP Summer Meeting.
4. *BP Statistical Review*, 1972.
5. *Japan Times*, 12th May 1973, p. 5.
6. Dev. Muraka (1973). *Evening Standard*, January.
7. D. C. Ion (1971). 'Arctic oil—one perspective', AAPG Arctic Symposium, San Francisco.
8. 'Uranium production and short-term demand', OECD, Paris, January 1969.
9. 'United States energy outlook; Summary Report of the National Petroleum Council', December 1972.
10. Advance copy of a paper being prepared for the Ninth World Energy Conference, 1974.
11. *The Times*, 10th April 1973.
12. Advance copy of a paper by Irwin M. Stelzer, Nat. Econ. Assoc., for Section 1, Ninth World Energy Conference, 1974.
13. D. C. Ion (1958). 'Interdependence in world-wide oil exploration', *Geophysics*, XXIII(2).
14. *Sunday Times*, 25th March 1973.

Discussion

H. Lucas (Lucas Petroleum (UK) Inc.): To finance the Petroleum Exploration Company whose only source of cash flow is from production revenues, it would seem that the wellhead price for gas should be allowed to rise until it is approximately equal to that of oil on a Btu heat content basis. Regardless of whether the company is successful in finding oil or gas either must be transported to market, with such costs being of about the same order of magnitude.

The general principle of equality of oil and gas wellhead prices would seem to apply in both the North Sea and America, both of which currently have highly regulated controls which have prevented the price of gas rising to its heat content equivalent, thus restricting supply and causing shortage conditions to develop.

J. H. Lichtblau (Petroleum Industry Research Foundation, Inc., New York): My comment would be that if gas prices rise to the same Btu heat content basis as oil prices at the wellhead you would not be able to sell much gas because transportation of gas is much more costly than transportation of oil. So on a Btu equivalent basis you might sell gas locally in the area where it is found but gas cannot be transported competitively over long distances. For that reason alone there's no argument for equating the price of gas and oil at the wellhead. But they should be equated in the market—and they're not. They haven't been in the past—gas has been considerably cheaper than oil—at least it has been in the US market where the two have to compete. The price of gas in the US has been set not by market forces but by Government control. I think that gas prices should be revised to a level which will relate them directly to the market price of oil, but also take into account the special premium qualities of gas as an absolutely clean fuel that requires no storage.

Mr M. W. Clegg (British Petroleum Co. Ltd): I would like to make two points: First, in defence of King Hubbert and his logistic curves, using the parameter derived by him for the curves relating to US reserves and production which were published in 1962, the 1970 data can be reproduced to within one or two %. This is a very good prediction.

Secondly, Mr Ion implies that the geologist has only to search and new reserves will be found. If one assumes that new additions to reserves over the next two decades are made at a rate of 20 billion barrels per year (which is slightly more than over the past decade), and allowing reserves to production ratios to fall to 15:1 or even 10:1, then it will be impossible to maintain the traditional growth rates for oil beyond the mid-1980s. In view of the fact that the Middle East contains some 70% of known reserves, and as an oil province it is unique, does Mr Ion consider it reasonable to assume that future successes will match those of the past?

Mr D. C. Ion: I see no reason why they should not. The point I was really trying to make was that one does need to go out and look for oil.

The point about the accuracy of King Hubbert's forecast is that you can also look at projections made earlier than 1960 (when King Hubbert made his projection) and find that there are other earlier forecasts which show just as close a correlation with what actually happened.

The problem is really the technological one. I have a greater faith in human ingenuity and skills than appears to be the opinion of many others. There have been these leaps forward and they have come as new ideas. I know the number of areas that have potential are naturally being reduced by past successes. But I still believe that we have not come to the end of the road of finding new oil and I do not believe that the total ultimate reserves are stabilised about the figure which Dr Gaskell holds. Lewis Weeks made a very detailed study on the basis of information that we had at the beginning of the war. Since then as Dr Gaskell's list shows, Weeks has from time to time increased these estimates. He has never to my knowledge had the opportunity to do a detailed study with new knowledge now available, as he did originally. In other words he has merely increased his number by adding in the offshore and estimating other new factors. Any estimate is like a spot check of a continually changing situation—rather like a still taken from a continuing film. So next year Lewis Weeks may write a new paper, in which he increases his numbers. People will believe in them—which proves the existence of the trap of accepting existing figures.

Closing Remarks

GEOFFREY CHANDLER

President of the Institute of Petroleum

One or two people have said to me that this is the best Summer Meeting they have ever attended. Now, if this is so thanks are of course due to the speakers, to the participants in the discussions and to the chairmen, all of whom have maintained very high standards for the debate has never flagged. In expressing thanks as I do most warmly to them, I would like to mention the Secretariat of the Institute, Colin Maynard and Joan Cummings without whom this event would never have taken place; and also Ken Inglis and Frank Hodges who were the guts of the organising committee and again got the meeting off the ground and shaped the whole programme.

One or two very brief concluding words. I think we have identified many areas of uncertainty but I think we all agree there is a changing energy scene today. And I think therefore that all of us who are concerned in the energy industry from whatever point of view, practical or academic, have a responsibility to discuss what we know from our own knowledge and experience, and to inform other people. Some of us will be wrong. Some of us will be right. But it is only by such an amalgam that truth will emerge. I think, as Dan Ion has said, that complementary interests in this field have been very firmly demonstrated by this meeting at which people from all parts of the energy industry have been represented.

I think what has been done in this meeting has been a serious contribution to thinking. I think there has been a convergence of views that energy is an area where positive action is required even though the timing and quantum of the problem that we may face is of course quite impossible to measure in precise terms. But the wise course would therefore seem to be to assume there is a possible problem ahead and take precautions against it rather than to do nothing. Economics could of course bring some solution on its own. It could without a prod be an uncomfortable solution if some of the question marks we have posed are answered in the wrong way. Therefore, a prod is required and if it is to be a useful prod it has to be given urgently because of the very long lead time both on the demand and supply side which just about every speaker has stressed. But again I would say that in the energy business evolution rather than revolution has characterised its course over time and I still think that evolution is likely to characterise it in future even if the pace of that evolution may sometimes seem to us to have a slightly revolutionary emphasis. I think we've all been made aware of the danger of generalisations and I think it is particularly healthy today to have problems which we have dealt with on a global basis brought down to a regional basis—from the macro to the more micro—and I would particularly like to thank the three regional contributors today.

I've been enormously impressed by the modesty of most of the contributors for I think the modesty with which projections of figures have been presented has added to the conviction that our authors have carried. It would be wrong to be selective about speakers but I would like to say that I believe the addresses from the Universities have opened windows to us which we as crude practitioners may not have observed as being in existence, and through which we might not look were they not brought to our attention.

Author Index

Subject Index